PROGRAMMING
THE 8086/8088

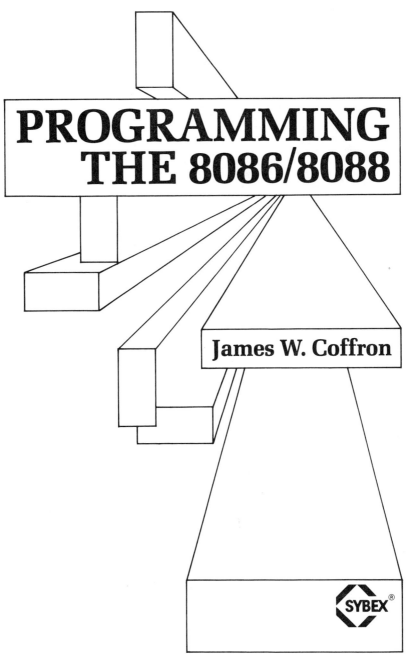

PROGRAMMING
THE 8086/8088

James W. Coffron

SYBEX®

San Francisco · Paris · Düsseldorf · London

Cover art by Jean Francois Penichoux
Design and layout by Ingrid Owen

Library of Congress Card Number: 83-50228
ISBN 0-89588-120-9
First Edition 1983
Printed in the United States of America
20   19   18   17   16   15   14   13   12

To Bill Long

CONTENTS

ACKNOWLEDGEMENTS

I wish to thank Bob Schuchard and Richard King, for their review and helpful suggestions; and my wife Carol, for preparing the original diagrams. Finally, a hearty thanks to the entire staff at Sybex for their splendid efforts.

INTRODUCTION

Welcome to the exciting world of 16-bit microprocessors. Imagine yourself programming, controlling, and using one of the most powerful and versatile 16-bit microprocessors: the 8086. This microprocessor can access over ONE MILLION memory locations—a far cry from the 64 thousand available in the majority of 8-bit microprocessors.

The 8086 is one of the most widely-used, 16-bit microprocessors in industry today. It has an extremely powerful instruction set that allows you to make your own software application a reality. In fact, the 8086 has two instructions that allow you to directly multiply and divide numbers; thus lengthy algorithms are no longer required to perform these tasks.

As you learn how to program the 8086, you will also be learning how to program the 8088 microprocessor. These two processors have identical instruction sets, and software written for one can be run on the other with no changes.

Both the 8086 and 8088 are well suited for communication with I/O devices and I/O ports. In fact, their architecture can support over 64,000 unique input and output ports. These ports can be any combination of 8 or 16 bits wide!

In addition, the 8086 and 8088 offer a powerful interrupt scheme, which allows you to vector to any system address for service routines. There are special interrupt vectors for single stepping and for internal errors, such as division by zero. Further, any of the interrupt service routines can be evoked via hardware or software.

The 8086 and 8088 are designed for ease of use in multiprocessor system applications. In light of this, Intel Corporation has designed several co-processors for use with the 8086/8088.

The preceding topics and more will be covered in this text. You will learn to program the 8086/8088 inside and out. From the internal microprocessor architecture to the advanced addressing modes, you will be shown how it all works. Each instruction will be described and several examples of actual programs will be given. To add more "real world" explanation, we will actually present examples of programs written for the IBM® PC, that use the 8088 microprocessor.

So, whether you are a beginner in microprocessor assembly-language programming or an advanced programmer, there is something for you in this text. After reading this book, you should be able to program the 8086/8088 for any application. In addition you should find that the text will serve as a valuable reference later on.

So let's get going! Let's start down the path that will lead you to an understanding of the power contained in one of the most advanced 16-bit microprocessors in use today.

CHAPTER BREAKDOWN

Chapter 1 starts off with a review of the basic concepts of microprocessor programming. It covers number representation, the addition and subtraction of binary and BCD numbers, and the use of flags.

Chapter 2 describes in general, the internal structure of a microprocessor; and discusses, in particular, the internal registers of the 8086/8088. An in-depth discussion focuses on the differences and similarities between the 8086 and 8088, and microprocessors in general.

Chapter 3 details the physical memory organizations of the 8086 and 8088 microprocessors—and shows that they are completely different. In addition, this chapter examines the different addressing modes for the various instructions.

Chapter 4 is a big one. It gives a complete listing of each instruction for the 8086/8088 and provides the relevant information pertaining to each instruction.

Chapter 5 discusses the basic programming techniques for microprocessors—addition, subtraction, multiplication, and division—and shows how these techniques are accomplished using the 8086/8088 instructions.

Chapter 6 discusses the general topic of interrupts for a microprocessor system and describes the complete interrupt structure for the 8086/8088. By the end of this chapter you will have a good understanding of how interrupts are used with these CPUs.

Chapter 7 covers the input and output techniques for the 8086/8088. Various input and output instructions are discussed and their uses examined. Included are programs for controlling an 8255 PIO and an 8253 counter timer LSI device.

Chapter 8 gets into "real world" applications. It shows you how to use the information on the 8088 to control the IBM PC. Two different application programs are given. Each uses the IBM BIOS to control the printer, the keyboard, and the RS-232 port.

Chapter 9 explores various program development techniques. Development hardware is evaluated and trade-offs are discussed. The chapter concludes with a discussion of assembly language details which you will be needing to write programs for the 8086/8088 CPU.

Also included are four useful appendices. **Appendix A** is a hexadecimal conversion table. **Appendix B** is an ASCII conversion table. **Appendix C** a decimal-to-BCD conversion table. **Appendix D** is an 8086/8088 instruction set summary.

1   BASIC CONCEPTS

INTRODUCTION

We shall begin with a discussion of the basic concepts and definitions used in computer programming. If you are already familiar with these concepts, you may only want to glance quickly at the contents of this chapter and then move on to Chapter 2. We do suggest, however, that even if you are an experienced programmer, you read through this chapter in order to familiarize yourself with the approach used throughout this book.

WHAT IS PROGRAMMING?

Given a problem, one normally tries to devise a solution. When this solution is expressed as a step-by-step procedure, it is called an *algorithm*. An algorithm may be expressed in any language or symbolism. It must terminate in a finite number of steps. Here is a simple example of an algorithm for unlocking and opening a door:

1. Insert key in the keyhole

2. Turn key one full turn to the left

3. Grasp doorknob

4. Turn doorknob, and push on the door

At this point, if the algorithm is correct for the type of lock involved, the door will open.

Once a solution to a problem has been expressed in the form of an algorithm, the next step is to translate it into a language that is understood by the computer.

At this point in time, only a well-defined subset of a natural language—called a *programming language*—is "understood" by computers. The conversion of an algorithm into a sequence of instructions comprising a programming language is called *programming*. The actual translation phase of the algorithm into the programming language is called *coding*. Programming refers not just to the coding, but also to the overall design of the programs and "data structures" that will implement the algorithm.

Effective programming requires not only an understanding of the possible implementation techniques for standard algorithms, but also the skillful use of computer hardware resources (such as internal registers, memory, and peripheral devices) and a creative use of appropriate data structures. (*Note:* We will examine these techniques in the chapters that follow.)

Programming also requires a strict documentation discipline. Well-documented programs are understandable not only to the author later on, but also to other users. Documentation must be both internal and external. *Internal program documentation* refers to the comments used in the body of a program to explain its operation. *External documentation* refers to the design documents that are separate from the program, including written explanations, manuals, and flowcharts.

An intermediate step is almost always taken between the design of the *algorithm* and the creation of the *program*. This step is called *flowcharting*.

FLOWCHARTING

A flowchart is simply a symbolic representation of an algorithm, usually expressed as a sequence of rectangles and diamonds. On a flowchart, rectangles are used to represent *commands,* (or executable statements), and diamonds are used for *tests* such as: If information X is true, then take action A; if not, take action B. Figure 1.1 shows an example of a flowchart. We will not give a formal definition for flowcharts at this point; we will discuss flowcharting in more detail in Chapter 3.

Flowcharting is a highly recommended intermediate step between the specification of an algorithm and the actual coding of a solution. Remarkably, it has been observed that perhaps 10% of the programming population can write a program successfully without having to prepare a flowchart. Unfortunately, it has also been observed that 90% of the population believes it belongs to this 10%! The result, then, is that, on the average, 80% of the programs fail the first time they are run on a computer. (These percentages are naturally not meant to be accurate.) In short, most novice programmers seldom see the necessity for drawing a flowchart. Ignoring

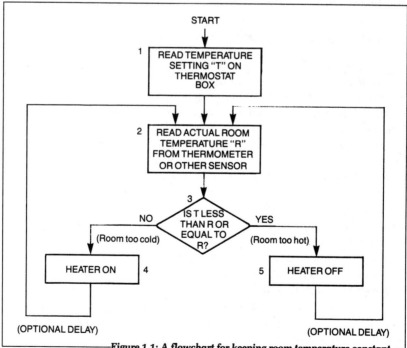

Figure 1.1: A flowchart for keeping room temperature constant.

the flowcharting step usually results in an erroneous program, and the programmer must then spend a long time testing and correcting his or her program. (This is known as the *debugging* phase.) The discipline of flowcharting is, therefore, highly recommended in all cases. Flowcharting generally requires a small amount of additional time prior to the coding, and usually results in a clear program that executes correctly within a short period of time. Once the procedure of flowcharting is well-understood, a small percentage of programmers can perform this step mentally, without using paper. Unfortunately, in such cases, the programs they write are usually difficult for others to understand, since the documentation normally provided with a flowchart is not available. It is universally recommended that flowcharting be used as a strict discipline for any program more than ten or fifteen instructions long. Many examples of flowcharting are provided throughout this book.

INFORMATION REPRESENTATION

All computers manipulate information in the form of numbers or characters. We will now examine the external and internal representations of information on a computer.

INTERNAL REPRESENTATION OF INFORMATION

Information in a computer is stored as groups of bits. A *bit* stands for *binary digit*. Because of the limitations of conventional electronics, the most practical representation of information uses two-state logic. The two states of the circuits used in digital electronics are generally "on" and "off." These states are represented logically by the symbols "0" and "1". Because these circuits are used to implement logical functions, they are called *binary logic circuits*. As a result, virtually all information processing today is performed in binary format. A group of eight bits is called a *byte*. A group of four bits is called a *nibble*.

Let us now see how information is represented internally in this binary format. Two entities must be represented inside the computer: the program (which is a sequence of instructions), and the data on which the program operates. The data may include numbers or alphanumeric text. Let's now discuss the representation of instructions, numbers, and alphanumerics in binary format.

Many of the examples that follow use eight bits. This makes it easier to explain the concept being discussed. The examples can easily be expanded to more than eight bits.

Representing Numeric Data   The representation of numbers in binary is not a straightforward task: several cases must be distinguished. We must be able to represent whole numbers, such as signed numbers (i.e., positive and negative numbers or integers) and numbers with decimal points. Let us now address these requirements and possible solutions.

Integers may be represented using a *direct binary* representation. The direct binary representation is simply the representation of the decimal value of a number in the binary system. In the binary system, the right-most bit represents 2 to the power 0. The next bit to the left represents 2 to the power 1; the next, 2 to the power 2; and the left-most bit, 2 to the power 7, which equals 128. For example,

$$b_7b_6b_5b_4b_3b_2b_1b_0$$

represents

$$b_72^7 + b_62^6 + b_52^5 + b_42^4 + b_32^3 + b_22^2 + b_12^1 + b_02^0$$

The powers of 2 are:

$$2^7 = 128, 2^6 = 64, 2^5 = 32, 2^4 = 16, 2^3 = 8, 2^2 = 4, 2^1 = 2, 2^0 = 1$$

The binary representation is analogous to the decimal representation of numbers. For example, 123 represents:

```
   1 × 100 = 100
 +2 ×  10 =  20
 +3 ×   1 =   3
             ───
             123
```

Note that $100 = 10^2$, $10 = 10^1$, $1 = 10^0$. In this positional notation, each digit represents a power of 10. In the binary system, each binary digit or bit represents a power of 2, instead of a power of 10 as in the decimal system. Let's look at an example of binary. 00001001 in binary represents:

```
   1 ×   1 = 1      (2^0)
   0 ×   2 = 0      (2^1)
   0 ×   4 = 0      (2^2)
   1 ×   8 = 8      (2^3)
   0 ×  16 = 0      (2^4)
   0 ×  32 = 0      (2^5)
   0 ×  64 = 0      (2^6)
   0 × 128 = 0      (2^7)
            ─────
       or 9  in decimal
```

Let's look at some other examples. 10000001 represents:

$$
\begin{array}{rrr}
1 \times & 1 = & 1 \\
0 \times & 2 = & 0 \\
0 \times & 4 = & 0 \\
0 \times & 8 = & 0 \\
0 \times & 16 = & 0 \\
0 \times & 32 = & 0 \\
0 \times & 64 = & 0 \\
1 \times & 128 = & 128 \\
\hline
& \text{or } 129 & \text{\textit{in decimal}}
\end{array}
$$

Therefore, 10000001 represents the decimal number 129. Examining the binary representation of numbers makes it easy to understand why bits are numbered from 0 to 7, going from right to left. Bit 0 is b_0 and corresponds to 2^0. Bit 1 is b_1 and corresponds to 2^1, and so on. The binary equivalents of the numbers from 0 to 255 are shown in Figure 1.2.

Decimal to Binary   Conversely, we can compute the binary equivalent of 11 decimal:

$$
\begin{array}{ll}
11 \div 2 = 5 \text{ remains } 1 > 1 & \textit{(lowest bit)} \\
5 \div 2 = 2 \text{ remains } 1 > 1 & \\
2 \div 2 = 1 \text{ remains } 0 > 0 & \\
1 \div 2 = 0 \text{ remains } 1 > 1 & \textit{(highest bit)}
\end{array}
$$

The binary equivalent is 1011 (read the right-most column from bottom to top). The binary equivalent of a decimal number can be obtained by continually dividing by 2, until a quotient of 0 is obtained.

Operating on Binary Data   The arithmetic rules for binary numbers are straightforward. The rules for addition are:

$$
\begin{array}{rl}
0 + 0 = & 0 \\
0 + 1 = & 1 \\
1 + 0 = & 1 \\
1 + 1 = & (1)\,0
\end{array}
$$

where (1) denotes a "carry" of 1 (note that 10 is the binary equivalent of 2 decimal). Binary subtraction can be performed by "adding the complement." We will discuss binary subtraction once we learn how to represent negative numbers. Let's consider the following example involving addition:

$$
\begin{array}{rr}
(2) & 10 \\
+(1) & +01 \\
\hline
(3) & 11 \\
\end{array}
$$

Addition is performed just as in decimal, by adding the columns, from

DECIMAL	BINARY	DECIMAL	BINARY
0	00000000	32	00100000
1	00000001	33	00100001
2	00000010	•	
3	00000011	•	
4	00000100	•	
5	00000101	63	0011111
6	00000110	64	0100000
7	00000111	65	0100001
8	00001000	•	
9	00001001	•	
10	00001010	•	
11	00001011	127	01111111
12	00001100	128	10000000
13	00001101	129	10000001
14	00001110		
15	00001111	•	
16	00010000	•	
17	00010001	•	
•			
•			
•		254	11111110
31	00011111	255	11111111

Figure 1.2: Decimal-Binary Table.

right to left. First you add the right-most column:

```
  10
+ 01
─────
   1    (0 + 1 = 1. No carry.)
```

Then the next column:

```
  10
+ 01
─────
  11    (1 + 0 = 1. No carry.)
```

Let us now look at other examples of binary addition:

```
  0010  (2)        0011  (3)
+ 0001  (1)      + 0001  (1)
──────────       ──────────
  0011  (3)        0100  (4)
```

The last example illustrates the role of the carry. Looking at the right-most bits: 1 + 1 = (1) 0. A carry of 1 is generated, which must be added to the next bits:

```
  001  (column 0 has just been added)
+ 000
+   1  (carry)
────
= (1)0  (where (1) indicates a new carry into column 2)
```

The final result is 0100.

   Let's consider another example:

```
  0111        (7)
+ 0011      + (3)
──────      ─────
  1010       (10)
```

In this example, a carry is again generated, up to the left-most column.

   With eight bits, it is, therefore, possible to directly represent the numbers 00000000 to 11111111 (i.e., 0 to 255). Two limitations, however, should be immediately visible. First, we are only representing positive numbers. Second, the magnitude of these numbers is limited to 255, if we use only eight bits. Let's now address these limitations in turn.

Signed Binary   In a signed binary representation, the left-most bit is used to indicate the sign of the number. Traditionally, 0 is used to denote a *positive* number and 1 is used to denote a *negative* number. For example, 11111111 represents – 127, while 01111111 represents + 127. We can now represent positive and negative numbers, but we have reduced the maximum magnitude of these numbers to 127. As another example, 00000001 represents + 1 (the leading 0 is " + ", followed by 0000001 = 1) and 10000001 is – 1 (the leading 1 is " – ").

Let us now address the *magnitude* problem. In order to represent larger numbers, it is necessary to use a larger number of bits. For example, if we use sixteen bits (two bytes) to represent numbers, we will be able to represent numbers from – 32K to + 32K in signed binary. (1K in computer jargon represents 1,024.) Bit 15 is used for the sign, and the remaining 15 bits (bit 14 through bit 0) are used for the magnitude: 2^{15} = 32K.

If we wish to represent large integers, it is necessary to use a larger number of bytes internally. This is why most simple BASICs, and other languages, provide only a limited precision for integers. This way, they can use a shorter internal format for the numbers they manipulate. Better versions of BASIC and some other languages provide a larger number of significant decimal digits at the expense of a large number of bytes for each number.

Let us now solve another problem: speed efficiency. Let's perform an addition in the signed binary representation we have just introduced. We want to add + 7 and – 5.

> + 7 is represented by 00000111
> – 5 is represented by 10000101
> _____
> *The binary sum is:*   10001100, or – 12

This is not the correct result. The correct result is + 2. We have neglected the fact that in order to use this representation, special actions must be taken, depending on the sign. This results in increased complexity and reduced performance. In other words, the binary addition of signed numbers does not "work correctly." This is annoying. Clearly, the computer must not only represent information, but it must also perform arithmetic on it.

The solution to this problem is called the *two's complement* representation. We will use the two's complement representation, instead of the *signed binary* representation. Before we introduce two's complement, we will first introduce an intermediate step: *one's complement.*

One's Complement   In the one's complement representation, all positive integers are represented in their correct binary format. For example + 3 is represented as usual by 00000011. However, its complement, – 3, is obtained by complementing every bit in the original representation. Each

0 is transformed into a 1 and each 1 into a 0. In our example, the one's complement representation of – 3 is 11111100.

Let's look at another example:

+ 2 is 00000010
– 2 is 11111101

Note that, in this representation, positive numbers start with a 0 on the left, and negative numbers start with a 1 on the left. As a test, let's add – 4 and + 6:

$$
\begin{array}{ll}
-4 \text{ is} & 11111011 \\
+6 \text{ is} & 00000110 \\
\hline
\textit{The sum is: } (1) & 00000001
\end{array}
$$

where (1) indicates a carry. The correct result should be 2 or 00000010.

Let's try again:

$$
\begin{array}{ll}
-3 \text{ is} & 11111100 \\
-2 \text{ is} & 11111101 \\
\hline
\textit{The sum is: } (1) & 11111001
\end{array}
$$

or – 6, plus a carry. The correct result is – 5. The representation of – 5 is 11111010. It did not work.

This representation does represent positive and negative numbers; however, the result of an ordinary addition does not always come out correctly. We will now use another representation. It is evolved from the one's complement and is called the two's complement representation.

Two's Complement Representation   In the two's complement representation, positive numbers are represented, as usual, in signed binary, just like in one's complement. The difference lies in the representation of *negative numbers*. A negative number represented in two's complement is obtained by first computing the one's complement and then *adding one*. Let's examine an example:

Example: + 3 is represented in signed binary by 00000011. Its one's complement representation is 11111100. The two's complement is obtained by adding one. It is 11111101.

Let's try an addition:

$$
\begin{array}{ll}
(3) & 00000011 \\
+ (5) & + \ 00000101 \\
\hline
(8) & 00001000
\end{array}
$$

The result is correct.

Let's try a subtraction:

```
  (3)        00000011
(-5)       + 11111011
           11111110
```

Now, let's identify the result by computing the two's complement:

(The one's complement of 11111110 is)   00000001
                      (Adding 1) +   1
(Therefore, the two's complement is)   00000010 *(or +2)*

The result + 11111110 represents - 2. It is correct.

We have now tried addition and subtraction, and the results have been correct (ignoring the carry). It seems that two's complement works!

We will now add + 4 and - 3 (the subtraction is performed by adding the two's complement):

```
        +4 is  00000100
        -3 is  11111101
The result is: (1) 00000001
```

If we ignore the carry, the result is 00000001 (i.e., 1 in decimal). This is the correct result. Without giving the complete mathematical proof, we will simply state that this representation does work. In two's complement, it is possible to add or subtract signed numbers, regardless of the sign. Using the usual rules of binary addition, the result comes out correct, including the sign. The carry is ignored. This is a very significant advantage. If this were not the case, we would have to correct the result for sign every time, causing a much slower addition or subtraction time.

For the sake of completeness, let us state that two's complement is simply the most convenient representation to use for simpler processors, such as microprocessors. On more complex processors, other representations may be used. For example, one's complement may be used, but if one's complement is used, special circuity is required to "correct the result."

From this point on, all signed integers will be implicitly represented internally in two's complement notation. See Figure 1.3 for a table of two's complement numbers.

We will now offer examples that demonstrate the rules of two's complement. In particular, C denotes a possible carry (or borrow) condition. (It is bit 8 of the result.) V denotes a two's complement overflow; that is, it indicates when the sign of the result is changed "accidentally," because the

+	TWO'S COMPLEMENT CODE	−	TWO'S COMPLEMENT CODE
+ 127	01111111	− 128	10000000
+ 126	01111110	− 127	10000001
+ 125	01111101	− 126	10000010
. . .		− 125	10000011
		. . .	
+ 65	01000001	− 65	10111111
+ 64	01000000	− 64	11000000
+ 63	00111111	− 63	11000001
. . .		. . .	
+ 33	00100001	− 33	11011111
+ 32	00100000	− 32	11100000
+ 31	00011111	− 31	11100001
. . .		. . .	
+ 17	00010001	− 17	11101111
+ 16	00010000	− 16	11110000
+ 15	00001111	− 15	11110001
+ 14	00001110	− 14	11110010
+ 13	00001101	− 13	11110011
+ 12	00001100	− 12	11110100
+ 11	00001011	− 11	11110101
+ 10	00001010	− 10	11110110
+ 9	00001001	− 9	11110111
+ 8	00001000	− 8	11111000
+ 7	00000111	− 7	11111001
+ 6	00000110	− 6	11111010
+ 5	00000101	− 5	11111011
+ 4	00000100	− 4	11111100
+ 3	00000011	− 3	11111101
+ 2	00000010	− 2	11111110
+ 1	00000001	− 1	11111111
+ 0	00000000		

— *Figure 1.3: A Two's Complement Table.* —

numbers are too large. It is an essentially internal carry from bit 6 to bit 7 (the sign bit). This will be clarified below.

Let us now demonstrate the role of the carry C and the overflow V.

The Carry C   Here is an example of a carry:

```
    (128)           10000000
  + (129)         + 10000001
  ─────────────────────────
  (257) = (1)       00000001
```

where (1) indicates a carry. The result requires a ninth bit (bit 8, since the right-most bit is 0). It is the carry bit.

If we assume that the carry is the ninth bit of the result, we recognize the result as binary 100000001 = 257. However, the carry must be recognized and handled with care. Inside the microprocessor, the registers used to hold information are generally only eight bits wide. When storing the result, only bits 0 to 7 will be preserved.

A carry, therefore, always requires special action. It must be detected by special instructions, then processed. Processsing the carry means either storing it somewhere (with a special instruction), ignoring it, or deciding that it is an error (if the largest authorized result is 11111111).

Overflow V   Here's an example of overflow:

```
 bit 6 ┐
 bit 7 ┐│
       ▼▼
    01000000          (64)
 (+)01000001        + (65)
 ─────────────────────────
    10000001         (-127)
```

An internal carry has been generated from bit 6 into bit 7. This is called an *overflow*. The result is now negative, "by accident." This situation must be detected, so that it can be corrected.

Let us examine another situation:

```
     11111111          (-1)
   + 11111111        + (-1)
 ─────────────────────────
 (1) 11111110          (-2)
   ↓
 carry
```

In this case, an internal carry has been generated from bit 6 into bit 7, and also from bit 7 into C. The rules of two's complement arithmetic specify that this carry should be ignored. The result is then correct. This is because the carry from bit 6 to bit 7 did not change the sign bit.

The carry from bit 6 into bit 7 is not an *overflow* condition. When operating on negative numbers, the overflow is not simply a carry from bit 6 into bit 7. Let's examine one more example:

$$
\begin{array}{ll}
11000000 & (-64) \\
\underline{+\ 10111111} & (-65) \\
(1)\ 01111111 & (+127)
\end{array}
$$

↓
carry

This time, there has been no internal carry from bit 6 into bit 7, but there has been an external carry. The result is incorrect, as bit 7 has been changed. An overflow condition should be indicated.

Overflow will occur in four situations, including:

1. the addition of large positive numbers

2. the addition of large negative numbers

3. the subtraction of a large positive number from a large negative number

4. the subtraction of a large negative number from a large positive number.

Let us now improve our definition of the overflow.

Technically, the overflow indicator, a special bit reserved for this purpose, and called a *condition code*, will be set when there is a carry from bit 6 into bit 7, and there is no external carry. It will also be set when there is no carry from bit 6 into bit 7, but there is an external carry. This indicates that bit 7—the sign of the result—has been accidentally changed. For the technically-minded reader, the overflow flag is set by Exclusive ORing the carry-in and carry-out of bit 7 (the sign bit). Practically every microprocessor is supplied with a special overflow flag to automatically detect this condition—a condition that requires corrective action.

Overflow indicates that the result of an addition or subtraction requires more bits than are available in the standard 8-bit register used to contain the result.

The Carry and the Overflow   The carry and the overflow bits are called *condition codes*. They are provided in every microprocessor. We will learn to use them for effective programming in Chapter 2. These two indicators are located in a special register called the flags or "status" register. This register also contains additional indicators (as described in Chapter 4).

Examples   We will now look at actual examples that illustrate the operation of the carry and the overflow. In each example, the symbol V denotes the overflow, and C denotes the carry. If there has been no overflow, V will equal 0. If there has been an overflow, V will equal 1 (the same is true for the carry C). Remember that the rules of two's complement specify that the carry be ignored. (The mathematical proof is not supplied here.) Let's examine the following examples:

Positive-Positive

```
  00000110              (+  6)
+ 00001000              (+ 8)
  00001110              (+ 14)      V:0  C:0
(CORRECT)
```

Positive-Positive with Overflow

```
  01111111              (+ 127)
+ 00000001              (+ 1)
  10000000              (- 128)     V:1  C:0
(ERROR)
```

The above is invalid because an overflow has occurred.

Positive-Negative (result positive)

```
   00000100             (+ 4)
 + 11111110             (- 2)
(1)00000010             (+ 2)       V:0  C:1 (disregard)
(CORRECT)
```

Positive-Negative (result negative)

```
  00000010              (+ 2)
+ 11111100              (- 4)
  11111110              (- 2)       V:0  C:0
(CORRECT)
```

Negative-Negative

```
   11111110             (- 2)
 + 11111100             (- 4)
(1)11111010             (- 6)       V:0  C:1 (disregard)
(CORRECT)
```

Negative-Negative with Overflow

```
    10000001              (-127)
  + 11000010              (-62)
  (1)01000011             (+67)        V:1  C:1
  (ERROR)
```

In the last examples, an "underflow" has occurred, by adding two large negative numbers. The result is -189, which is too large to reside in eight bits.

Fixed Format Representation   We now know how to represent signed integers; however, we have not yet resolved the problem of magnitude. If we want to represent larger integers, we will need several bytes. In order to perform arithmetic operations efficiently, it is necessary to use a fixed number of bytes, rather than a variable number. Therefore, once the number of bytes is chosen, the maximum magnitude of the number that can be represented is fixed.

THE MAGNITUDE PROBLEM

Let us consider the following important point: the number of bits, n, chosen for the two's complement representation is usually fixed for that program. If any result or intermediate computation should generate a number that requires more than n bits, some bits will be lost. The program normally retains the n left-most bits (the most significant) and drops the low-order ones. This is called *truncating* the result.

Let's look at an example in the decimal system, using a six-digit representation:

```
        123456
  ×        1.2
        246912
      123456
      148147.2
```

The result requires seven digits. The 2 after the decimal point will be dropped, and the final result will be 148147. It has been truncated. Usually, as long as the position of the decimal point is not lost, this method is used to extend the range of the operations that can be performed, at the expense of precision. The problem is the same in binary. This fixed-format representation may cause a loss of precision, but it may be sufficient for usual computations or mathematical operations.

Unfortunately, in the case of accounting, no loss of precision is tolerable.

For example, if a customer rings up a large total on a cash register, it would not be acceptable to have a five-figure total that would be approximated to the dollar. Thus, another representation must be used whenever precision in the result is essential. The solution normally used is BCD, or binary-coded decimal.

BCD Representation The principle used in representing numbers in BCD is to encode each decimal digit separately and to use as many bits as necessary to represent the complete number exactly. To encode each of the digits from 0 through 9, four bits are necessary. (Three bits supply only eight combinations and, therefore, cannot encode the ten digits.) Four bits allow sixteen combinations and are, therefore, sufficient to encode the digits 0 through 9. It should also be noted that six of the possible codes will not be used in the BCD representation (see Figure 1.4). This will result later on in a potential problem, when performing additions and subtractions. Since only four bits are needed to encode a BCD digit, two BCD digits may be encoded in every byte. This is called *packed BCD*. As an example, 00000000 is 00 in BCD. 10011001 is 99.

A BCD code is read as follows:

```
              0010        0001
BCD digit 2 ◄──────────┘        │
BCD digit 1 ◄──────────────────┘
BCD number 21
```

As many bytes as necessary will be used to represent all BCD digits. Typically, one or more nibbles will be used at the beginning of the representation to indicate the total number of nibbles (i.e., the total number of BCD digits used). Another nibble or byte will be used to denote the position

CODE	BCD SYMBOL	CODE	BCD SYMBOL
0000	0	1000	8
0001	1	1001	9
0010	2	1010	UNUSED
0011	3	1011	UNUSED
0100	4	1100	UNUSED
0101	5	1101	UNUSED
0110	6	1110	UNUSED
0111	7	1111	UNUSED

Figure 1.4: A BCD Table.

of the decimal point. However, conventions may vary. Here is an example
of a representation for multibyte BCD integers:

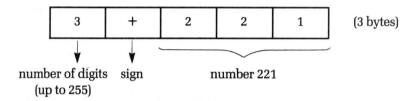

This example represents + 221. (The sign may be represented by 0000 for
+ , and 0001 for − , for example.)

The BCD representation can easily accommodate decimal numbers. For
example, + 2.21 may be represented by:

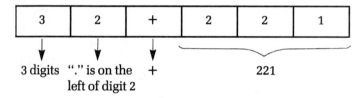

The advantage of BCD is that it yields absolutely correct results. Its
disadvantage is that it uses a large amount of memory and results in slow
arithmetic operations. This is acceptable only in an accounting environment, but BCD is normally not used in other cases.

We have now solved the problems associated with the representation of
integers, signed integers, and large integers. We have even presented one
possible method of representing decimal numbers, with BCD representation. Let us now examine the problem of representing decimal numbers in
fixed length format.

Floating-Point Representation   The basic principle of floating point representation is that decimal numbers are represented with a fixed length
format. In order not to waste bits, the representation will *normalize* all the
numbers. For example, 0.000123 wastes three zeroes on the left before
non-zero digits. These zeroes have no meaning except to indicate the position of the decimal point. Normalizing this number results in $.123 \times 10^{-3}$.
.123 is the *normalized mantissa*; − 3 is the *exponent*. We have normalized
this number by eliminating all the meaningless zeroes to the left of the first
non-zero digit and by adjusting the exponent. Let's consider another

example:

Example: 22.1 is normalized as .221 × 10². The general form of floating-point representation is M × 10^E, where M is the mantissa, and E is the exponent.

It can be readily seen that a normalized number is characterized by a mantissa less than 1 and greater than or equal to .1 in all cases where the number is not zero. In other words, it can be represented mathematically by:

$$.1 \leqslant M < 1 \text{ or } 10^{-1} \leqslant M < 10^0$$

Similarly, in the binary representation:

$$2^{-1} \leqslant \quad M < \quad 2^0 \text{ (or } .5 \leqslant M < 1)$$

where M is the absolute value of the mantissa (disregarding the sign). For example:

111.01 is normalized as: .11101 × 2³.

The mantissa is 11101. The exponent is 3.

Now that we have defined the principle of the representation, let us examine the actual format. A typical floating-point representation appears in Figure 1.5.

In the representation in Figure 1.5, four bytes are used for a total of 32 bits. The first byte on the left of the illustration is used to represent the exponent. Both the exponent and the mantissa will be represented in two's complement. As a result, the maximum exponent will be – 128. "S" in Figure 1.5 denotes the sign bit.

Three bytes are used to represent the mantissa. Since the first bit in the two's complement representation indicates the sign, this leaves 23 bits for the representation of the magnitude of the mantissa.

This is only one example of a floating point representation. It is possible to use only three bytes, or it is possible to use more. The 4-byte representation proposed above is a common one that represents a reasonable compromise in terms of accuracy, magnitude of numbers, storage utilization, and efficiency in arithmetic operation.

We have now explored the problems associated with the representation of numbers and have learned how to represent them in integer form with a

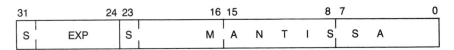

Figure 1.5: Typical Floating-Point Representation.

sign, or in decimal form. Let's now go on to examine how alphanumeric data is represented internally.

Representing Alphanumeric Data   The representation of alphanumeric data (i.e., characters) is completely straightforward: all characters are encoded in an 8-bit code. Only two codes are in general use in the computer world, the ASCII Code and the EBCDIC Code. ASCII stands for "American Standard Code for Information Interchange," and is universally used in the world of microprocessors. EBCDIC is a variation of ASCII used by IBM, and is, therefore, not used in the microcomputer world unless one interfaces to an IBM terminal.

Let us briefly examine the ASCII encoding. We encode 26 letters of the alphabet for both upper and lower case, plus 10 numeric symbols, and perhaps 20 additional special symbols. This can be easily accomplished with 7 bits, which allow 128 possible codes. (See Figure 1.6) All characters are, therefore, encoded in 7 bits. The 8th bit, when it is used, is the *parity bit*.

HEX	MSD	0	1	2	3	4	5	6	7
LSD	BITS	000	001	010	011	100	101	110	111
0	0000	NUL	DLE	SPACE	0	@	P	—	p
1	0001	SOH	DC1	!	1	A	Q	a	q
2	0010	STX	DC2	"	2	B	R	b	r
3	0011	ETX	DC3	#	3	C	S	c	s
4	0100	EOT	DC4	$	4	D	T	d	t
5	0101	ENQ	NAK	%	5	E	U	e	u
6	0110	ACK	SYN	&	6	F	V	f	v
7	0111	BEL	ETB	'	7	G	W	g	w
8	1000	BS	CAN	(	8	H	X	h	x
9	1001	HT	EM	)	9	I	Y	i	y
A	1010	LF	SUB	*	:	J	Z	j	z
B	1011	VT	ESC	+	;	K	[	k	{
C	1100	FF	FS	,	<	L	\	l	--
D	1101	CR	GS	—	=	M	]	m	}
E	1110	SO	RS	.	>	N	^	n	~
F	1111	SI	US	/	?	O		o	DEL

Figure 1.6: ASCII Conversion Table (See Appendix B for Abbreviations.)

Parity is a technique for verifying that the contents of a byte have not been accidentally changed. The number of 1's in the byte are counted and the 8th bit is set to one if the count was odd, thus making the total even. This is called *even parity. Odd parity* (i.e., writing the 8th bit [the left-most bit] so that the total number of 1's in the byte is odd) can also be used.

As an example, let us compute the parity bit for 0010011 using even parity. The number of 1's is 3. The parity bit must, therefore, be a 1, so that the total number of bits is 4, or even. The result is 10010011, where the leading 1 is the parity bit and 0010011 identifies the character.

The table of 7-bit ASCII codes is shown in Figure 1.6. In practice, it is used "as is," without parity, by adding a 0 in the left-most position, or else with parity, by adding the appropriate extra bit on the left.

In specialized situations, such as telecommunications, other codings, such as error-correcting codes, may be used. However, descriptions of these codings are beyond the scope of this book.

Now that we have examined the usual representations for both program and data inside the computer, let us examine the possible external representations.

EXTERNAL REPRESENTATION OF INFORMATION

The external representation of information refers to the way information is presented to the *user*, i.e., generally to the programmer. Information may be presented externally in essentially three formats: binary, octal or hexadecimal, and symbolic. Let's examine these formats.

1. Binary   We have seen that information is stored internally in *bytes*, which are sequences of eight *bits* (0's or 1's). It is sometimes desirable to display this internal information directly in its binary format—this is known as *binary representation*. A simple example is provided by light-emitting diodes (LEDs) which are essentially miniature lights on the front panel of a microcomputer. In the case of an 8-bit microprocessor, a front panel will typically be equipped with eight LEDs to display the contents of any internal register. A lighted LED indicates a 1. An unlighted LED indicates a 0. Such a binary representation may be used for the fine debugging of a complex program, especially if it involves input/output, but is naturally impractical at the human level. This is because in most cases, it is easier to look at information in symbolic form. For example, 9 is much easier to understand and to remember than 1001. More convenient representations have been devised, which improve the interface between people and machines.

2. Octal and Hexadecimal   Octal and hexadecimal encode three and four binary bits, respectively, into a unique symbol. Octal is a format using three bits, where each combination of three bits is represented by a symbol between 0 and 7. (See Figure 1.7)

For example, 00 100 100 binary is represented by:

or 044 in octal.

As another example: 11 111 111 is:

$$\downarrow \quad \downarrow \quad \downarrow$$
$$3 \quad 7 \quad 7$$

or 377 in octal.

Conversely, the octal 211 represents

010 001 001

or 10001001 binary.

Octal has traditionally been used on older computers that employ various numbers of bits, ranging from 8 to, perhaps, 64. More recently, with the dominance of 8-bit microprocessors, the 8-bit format has become the standard, and another, more practical, representation is used—hexadecimal representation.

In the hexadecimal representation, a group of four bits is encoded as one hexadecimal digit. Hexadecimal digits are represented by the symbols

BINARY	OCTAL
000	0
001	1
010	2
011	3
100	4
101	5
110	6
111	7

Figure 1.7: Octal Symbols.

from 0 to 9, and by the letters A, B, C, D, E, F. For example, 0000 is represented by 0; 0001 is represented by 1; and 1111 is represented by the letter
F (see Figure 1.8). For example, 1010 0001 in binary is represented by

A   1

in hexadecimal.

Hexadecimal offers the advantage of encoding eight bits into only two
digits. This is easier to visualize or memorize and faster to type into a computer than its binary equivalent. Therefore, on most new microcomputers,
hexadecimal is the preferred method of representation for groups of bits.

Naturally, whenever the information present in the memory has a meaning, such as representing text or numbers, hexadecimal is not convenient
for representing the meaning of this information for a human user.

Symbolic Representation   *Symbolic representation* refers to the external representation of information in actual symbolic form. For example,

DECIMAL	BINARY	HEX	OCTAL
0	0000	0	0
1	0001	1	1
2	0010	2	2
3	0011	3	3
4	0100	4	4
5	0101	5	5
6	0110	6	6
7	0111	7	7
8	1000	8	10
9	1001	9	11
10	1010	A	12
11	1011	B	13
12	1100	C	14
13	1101	D	15
14	1110	E	16
15	1111	F	17

Figure 1.8: Hexadecimal Codes

decimal numbers are represented as decimal numbers, and not as sequences of hexadecimal symbols or bits. Similarly, text is represented as such. Naturally, symbolic representation is most practical to the user. It is used whenever an appropriate display device is available, such as a CRT display or a printer. (A CRT display is a television-type screen used to display text or graphics.) Unfortunately, in smaller systems, such as one-board microcomputers, it is uneconomical to provide such displays, and the user is restricted to hexadecimal communication with the computer.

Summary of External Representations   Symbolic representation of information is the most desirable, since it is the most natural for a human user. However, it requires an expensive interface in the form of an alpha-numeric keyboard, plus a printer or a CRT display. For this reason, it may not be available on the less expensive systems. An alternative type of representation is then used and in such a case, hexadecimal is the dominant representation. Only in rare cases, relating to fine debugging at the hardware or software level, is the binary representation used. *Binary* directly displays the contents of the registers of memory in binary format.

  Now that we have seen how information is represented internally and externally, let's go on to examine the actual microprocessor that manipulates this information.

2 INSIDE THE 8086/8088

INTRODUCTION

In this chapter we will discuss the internal architecture of the 8086/8088 microprocessor. We will begin with a broad discussion of the architecture of a microprocessor in general. We will then discuss important concepts common to most *single-chip* microprocessors.

Next, we will examine the instruction cycle of a typical microprocessor. By the end of this discussion you should have a good general understanding of the internal organization of a microprocessor and the execution of instructions.

We will then go on to examine the internal organizations of the 8086/8088. We will look closely at the many features provided by these two processors and contrast them with features typical of other microprocessors. When comparing processors, it can be clearly seen that the designers of the 8086/8088 have implemented new solutions to old problems, and this has resulted in an easy-to-use, extremely powerful microprocessor.

GENERAL MICROPROCESSOR SYSTEM ARCHITECTURE

Let's begin our discussion by examining the general hardware architecture of a typical microprocessor-based system. Although we will not take the time now to explain how this architecture is realized with the 8086/8088, we will show how a microprocessor fits into a system environment and thereby help you to better understand the internal organization of a CPU.

Figure 2.1 displays a block diagram of a typical microprocessor-controlled system. Appearing on the left of the diagram is the *microprocessor unit* (the *MPU*)—in this case the 8086/8088—which implements the functions of the *central-processing unit* (the *CPU*) on a single chip. The CPU includes an *arithmetic-logical unit* (the *ALU*), plus its internal registers, and a *control unit* (the *CU*), which decodes and internally sequences instructions. (We will learn more about the CPU later in this chapter.) The MPU has three *buses*: an *address* bus, a *data* bus, and a *control* bus. A bus

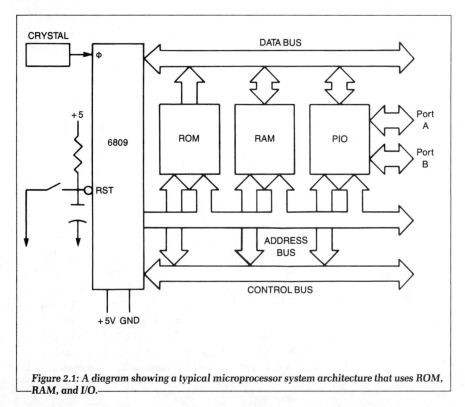

Figure 2.1: A diagram showing a typical microprocessor system architecture that uses ROM, RAM, and I/O.

is a collection of electronic signals that originate at a common source and perform a common function.

We can see in Figure 2.1 that alongside the CPU are the ROM, RAM, and I/O. These are the main blocks of a microprocessor system. No matter how complex a system is or what its function is, the block diagram of Figure 2.1 accurately depicts it.

Let us examine briefly each of the main blocks, labeled ROM, RAM, and I/O. The *ROM* (or read-only memory) stores the program of the system. The advantage of ROM memory is that its contents are permanent; they do not disappear when the system is turned off. For this reason, ROM usually contains the "bootstrap" or monitor program that permits initial system operation. In a process-control environment, nearly all programs reside in ROM. This is because they are seldom changed and must be protected against power failures.

RAM (or random access memory) is the read/write memory of the system. In a hobbyist or program-development environment, most of the programs reside in RAM, so they can be easily changed. Such programs can be kept in RAM or transferred into ROM, if desired. RAM is volatile. Information in RAM is lost when power is turned off. In a control system, the amount of RAM is typically small (for data only); however, in a program-development environment, the amount of RAM is generally large, as it contains programs, plus the development software. Prior to use, the contents of RAM must be loaded from an external device.

Finally, the system also contains one or more *interface chips*. An interface chip allows communication between the system and the external world. The PIO is a frequently-used interface chip. *PIO* stands for parallel input/output. PIOs, like the other chips in the system, connect to all three buses and provide data paths for communication with the outside world.

Let's now study the function of the buses.

THE THREE BUSES

As we mentioned previously, the system in Figure 2.1 has a 3-bus architecture. The *address bus* has the "job" of enabling the path for the communication between the CPU and ROM, RAM, or I/O. The *data bus* passes the actual information between the CPU and the enabled system block (see Figure 2.1). Finally, the *control bus* performs the dual task of 1) electrically defining the type of communication, and 2) beginning and ending the transfer.

In most applications the CPU controls each bus. It is the function of the CPU to correctly time each bus so that reliable communication can occur.

You, as the programmer, need not concern yourself with this activity, as it is done by the system hardware. However, you must provide the correct instructions to the CPU so that it can generate the right addresses and data to the system hardware. (As a programmer you can only assume that the hardware is functioning correctly.)

The width of a bus determines the number of signal lines contained in the group comprising the bus. For the 8086/8088 the address bus can be up to 20 bits wide. The width of the data bus is 16 bits and the width of the control bus varies, but it has a nominal value of 5 bits. The width of each bus differs from CPU to CPU, and from system to system.

INSIDE A MICROPROCESSOR

Let us now examine Figure 2.2 and discuss the general internal architecture of a microprocessor. In addition, we will show you how the 8086 and 8088 implement their specific internal architectures, and we will point out the similarities and differences to the general case (shown in Figure 2.2).

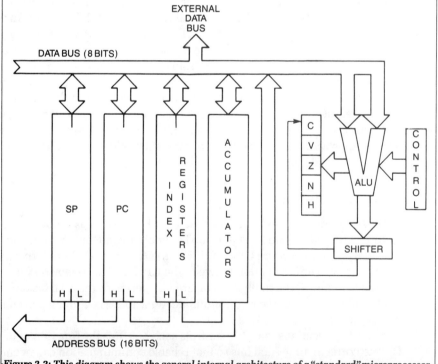

Figure 2.2: This diagram shows the general internal architecture of a "standard" microprocessor.

Figure 2.2 shows a diagram of a standard architecture of a general microprocessor. Let's examine the different modules in this figure. The *control box* (on the right of the illustration) represents the control unit that synchronizes the system hardware and timing.

To the left of the control box is the ALU. The *ALU* performs all arithmetic and logical operations. Special registers, called *accumulators,* are usually connected to the output of the ALU. They contain the results of arithmetic operations. In addition to the arithmetic and logical operations, the ALU also provides *shift* and *rotate* facilities. As illustrated in Figure 2.3, a shift moves the contents of the accumulator to the left or right by one or more positions. In this illustration, each bit has been moved to the left by one position.

Referring back to Figure 2.2, the *status* or *condition code register* appears to the left of the ALU. The job of this register is to store the internal conditions of the microprocessor in codes. The condition codes are sometimes referred to as *condition flags.* An example of this is a bit that indicates when the result of an operation performed by the ALU leaves all accumulator bits equal to 0. When this occurs, the condition flag called the *zero flag* is set to true.

The contents of the condition code register can be tested by specialized

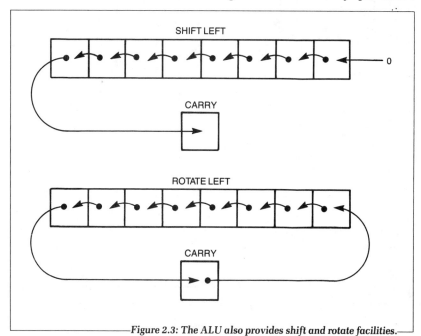

Figure 2.3: The ALU also provides shift and rotate facilities.

instructions. The CPU alters its execution path based on the logical values of these codes. We will discuss this subject in further detail when we present the instruction set and give program examples for the 8086/8088. (Note: most of the instructions executed by the microprocessor will modify some or all of the condition flags. The instruction set for the 8086/8088 [presented in Chapter 4] clearly indicates which instructions modify which condition flags.)

Moving to the left in Figure 2.2, we find the address registers. These registers are used for the storage of addresses. They are connected to the system address bus. Whenever the CPU executes a program, the address registers are combined logically to form a complete system address. Some of the power of a microprocessor comes from its ability to combine the address registers in special ways to form the system address present on the address bus. Chapter 3 describes in detail how the address registers of the 8086/8088 can be logically combined to form a single address. Figure 2.4 shows

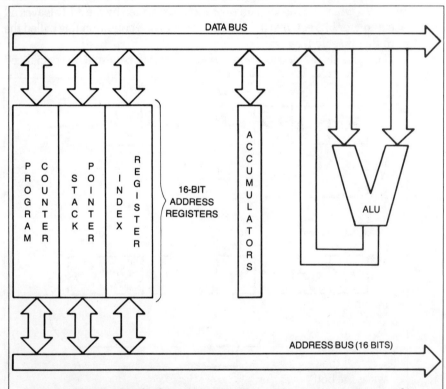

Figure 2.4: The PC, SP, and index registers are common microprocessor registers used in forming a complete system address.

three common address registers contained in a microprocessor: the program counter, the stack pointer, and the index register. Note that the registers also appear in Figure 2.2. Let's discuss them.

THE PROGRAM COUNTER (or PC)

The *program counter* (or *PC*) must be present in all microprocessors, as it is fundamental to program execution. It contains the address of the next instruction to be executed.

A program normally executes in a sequential fashion. To access the next instruction, it is necessary to "fetch" it from the system memory and read the instruction into the microprocessor. The contents of the PC are deposited on the address bus and input to the memory address line. The memory then reads the contents specified by the address and sends the corresponding instruction back to the CPU.

THE STACK POINTER (or SP)

The *stack pointer* (or *SP*) implements the system stack. (The stack is described in detail in a following section. The stack is often used for handling interrupts and subroutines, and for saving temporary data.) The stack pointer contains the memory address of the top of the stack.

THE INDEX REGISTER

Indexing is a memory-addressing facility used to access blocks of data in the memory, using only a single instruction. This facility is not available in all microprocessors. It is, however, available with the 8086/8088. An *index register* typically contains a displacement, which is automatically added to a base value when forming an address. In short, indexing is used to access a word within a block of data. Now that we have discussed all the elements in Figure 2.2, let's move on and discuss the stack.

THE STACK

A *stack*, formally called a LIFO (last-in, first-out) structure, is a set of memory locations, allocated to the stack data structure. The essential characteristic of the stack is that the first element introduced in the stack is always at the bottom, and the element most recently deposited is always on top.

An analogy can be drawn with plates stacked on a restaurant counter—assuming that there is a hole in the counter with a spring at the bottom, and that the plates are piled up in the hole. With this organization, it is guaranteed that the plate that was placed first in the stack is always at the bottom, and the most-recent placement is on top.

In normal use, a stack is only accessible via two operations or instructions: PUSH and POP. These two instructions are illustrated in Figure 2.5. The PUSH operation deposits elements on the top of the stack. A POP transfers the top element of the stack into the internal register specified by the instruction.

THE GENERAL INSTRUCTION CYCLE

Let's now examine Figure 2.6. This diagram illustrates the role of the program counter, which fetches an instruction from the memory. The microprocessor unit appears on the left of the illustration, and the memory appears on the right. The memory stores instructions and data. The memory chip can be either ROM, RAM, or any other chip that happens to contain memory.

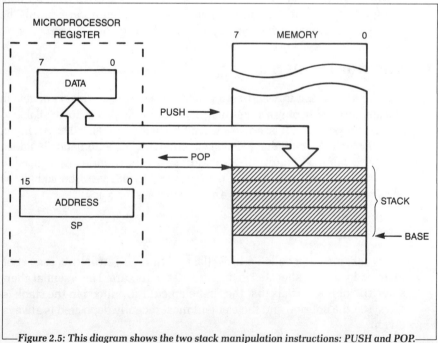

Figure 2.5: This diagram shows the two stack manipulation instructions: PUSH and POP.

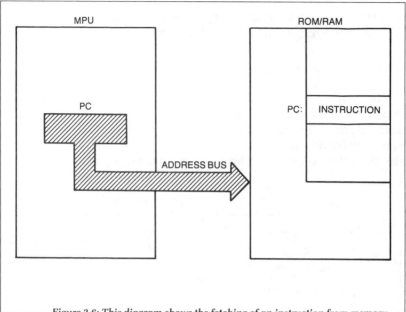

Figure 2.6: This diagram shows the fetching of an instruction from memory.

Viewing Figure 2.6, we will assume that the program counter holds an address, which is the address of the next instruction to be fetched from the memory.

Every microprocessor proceeds in three cycles, which involve:

1. fetching the next instruction

2. decoding the instruction

3. executing the instruction.

Let us now discuss each cycle.

FETCHING

In the first cycle, the contents of the program counter are placed on the system address bus and input to memory at the correct time. The control bus then generates a memory read signal. When the memory reaches the read signal, data stored in memory at the specified address is placed on the system data bus. The microprocessor then reads the information on the data bus into an internal register called the *instruction register* (or IR). The information read into the CPU is the instruction. We can say that the instruction has been fetched from memory. Figure 2.7 is a block diagram showing the fetching of an instruction from memory.

DECODING AND EXECUTING

Once the instruction is in the IR, the control unit of the microprocessor decodes it and generates the correct sequence of internal and external signals for its execution. Some time, typically one clock period, is necessary for the CPU to decode an instruction and logically decide what action to take. We will see later on that the 8086/8088 puts to good use this normally

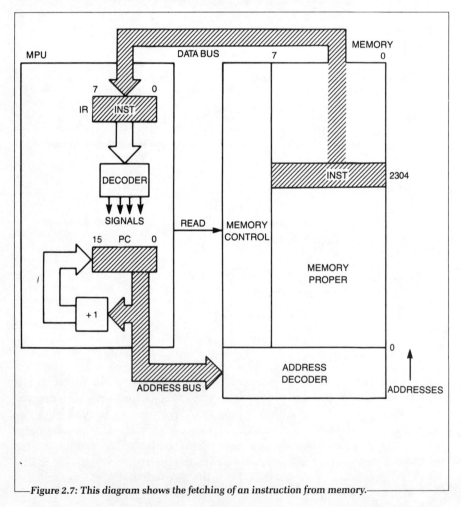

Figure 2.7: This diagram shows the fetching of an instruction from memory.

"idle" time (i.e., the time waiting for the CPU to decode the instruction).

Once the CPU has decoded the instruction, it then performs a series of events, dictated by the instruction. Some instructions require simple tasks and thus take little time to execute; others require several events to occur and thus take longer. The speed of execution for an instruction is usually expressed in the total number of clock cycles required for completion.

FETCHING THE NEXT INSTRUCTION

We have just described how an instruction is fetched from memory, using the program counter. During the execution of a program, instructions are fetched in sequence. It is, therefore, necessary for an automatic mechanism, called an *incrementer,* to be provided to fetch instructions in sequence. The incrementer is attached to the program counter, as shown in Figure 2.7.

It must be stressed that the preceding descriptions are simplified. In reality, some instructions may be two, three, or six bytes long and, in such cases, the PC must logically decide how many bytes are contained in each instruction, before the next instruction starts. We will be discussing more about the function of the PC as we detail the internal architecture of the 8086/8088.

INTERNAL ORGANIZATION OF THE 8086/8088

So far, we have discussed (in general terms) how a microprocessor system is organized, and we have examined the internal architecture of a CPU. Let us now build on this information and detail the actual internal architecture of the 8086/8088. Once you understand this program, it is much easier to understand the topic of addressing modes (presented in the following chapter).

The internal architectures of the 8086 and 8088 are virtually identical from a programming point of view. Software written for the 8086 will run on the 8088 with no modifications. The reverse is also true. (*Note:* It is important to note that the hardware implementation of each microprocessor is quite unique, but this is of little concern to us here, since we are concentrating on programming in this text.)

Figure 2.8 shows a functional block diagram of the 8086/8088. This diagram shows that there are two main functional logic blocks in the device: the BIU (bus interface unit) and the EU (execution unit). In the general block diagram back in Figure 2.2, both of these functions were grouped into a single control block. Let us examine what they do.

The major function of the BIU in the 8086/8088 is to provide the physical interface between the 8086/8088 and the "outside" world. The BIU controls the system address, data, and control buses. It can operate in parallel with the EU. One of the unique features of the BIU is its "instruction prefetch" capability. To understand what this means, consider the following.

When the PCU executes instructions, it first fetches the instruction from memory and then decodes it. During the decoding time the external buses of the CPU are idle. In other words, there is no activity on the buses because the CPU does not electrically know what to do, as the instruction has not yet been decoded.

In the 8086/8088, the BIU fetches an instruction from memory and then while the EU is decoding that instruction, the BIU gets the next instruction

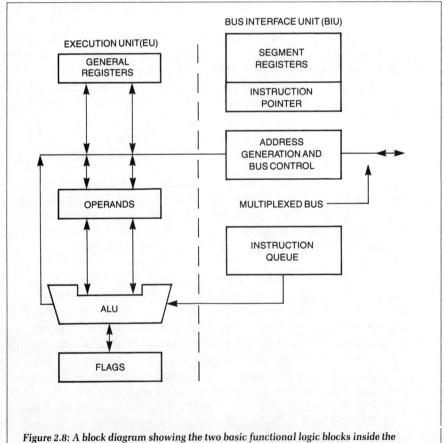

Figure 2.8: A block diagram showing the two basic functional logic blocks inside the 8086/8088. These are the EU (execution unit) and BIU (bus interface unit).

from memory. In this way, the next instruction is "prefetched" and waiting to be executed by the CPU. As a matter of fact, the 8086 can have up to six bytes of information in the instruction queue, while the 8088 can have up to four.

Some instructions on the 8086/8088 are executed completely internally in the CPU, and can require many clock cycles. An example of this type of instruction would be the DIVIDE instruction. During the time that the CPU is performing the division, the BIU is prefetching data from memory, up to the maximum number of bytes that can be held in the queue.

Prefetching data from memory reduces the overall instruction execution time. This is because the instruction fetch time does not have to be counted in the overall execution time. This statement is not always true, however, because there will be times when an entire instruction must be obtained without a prefetch. This occurs whenever the queue is flushed or reset. For example, whenever the 8086/8088 executes a jump instruction, the queue is flushed and must be filled again. If you are not familiar with the jump instruction, you may not understand why the queue must be flushed. This will be made clear when the instruction set is given in Chapter 4.

The other functional hardware section of the 8086/8088 shown in Figure 2.8 is the execution unit. This unit contains a 16-bit arithmetic logic unit. It maintains the condition flags of the CPU. The EU also manipulates the general registers of the CPU. All registers in the EU are 16 bits wide. This is true of both the 8086 and 8088.

8086/8088 GENERAL REGISTERS

Figure 2.9 shows the general registers of the 8086/8088. We can seen in this figure that there are two main groups: the data group, and the pointer and index group. Each register is 16 bits wide. The data group is labeled AX, BX, CX and DX. They can be used as a single 16-bit register or as two 8-bit registers. When used as two 8-bit registers, they are divided into an upper (H) and lower (L) half, labeled AH, AL, BH, BL, CH, CL, and DH, DL.

The pointer and index group of registers (shown in Figure 2.9) are used only as 16-bit registers. These registers are labeled SP (stack pointer), BP (base pointer), SI (source index), and DI (destination index). The reasoning behind these names will become clear later on in the text when we discuss the various addressing modes and show programming examples for the 8086/8088. For now, it is only important to know that these registers exist, and how they are organized.

SEGMENT REGISTERS

There are four segment registers in the 8086/8088, as shown in Figure 2.10. We will give a brief description of the segment registers now and a more detailed description in Chapter 3. Each segment register is 16 bits in length and each has a particular name: code segment (CS), data segment

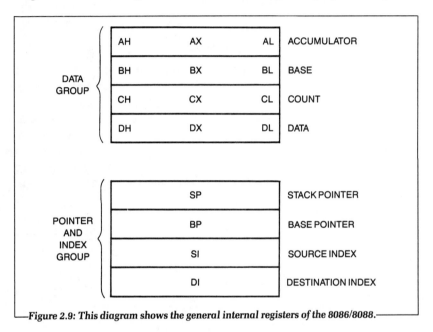

Figure 2.9: This diagram shows the general internal registers of the 8086/8088.

Figure 2.10: This diagram shows the four segment registers of the 8086/8088. These registers are logically combined with the general registers to form a 20-bit system address.

(DS), stack segment (SS) and extra segment (ES). The names are useful for understanding how the segment registers are used during program execution.

These registers are combined with other internal registers during program execution to form a complete 20-bit system address for the CPU external address bus. For example, when performing a PUSH or POP operation with the stack, the SS register is combined logically with other registers to form the memory address at points to the top of the stack. We will expand on this in the addressing mode discussion in Chapter 3.

INSTRUCTION POINTER

In the description of the general block diagram of a microprocessor shown in Figure 2.2, we discussed the operation of the program counter. In the 8086/8088 the program counter is replaced by the instruction pointer (IP) register. The IP register is updated by the BIU to point to the address of the next instruction. Programs do not have direct access to the instruction pointer; but, during execution of a program, the IP can be modified or saved and restored from the stack.

FLAGS

The 8086/8088 have six 1-bit status or condition flags that are updated by the EU. These flags, shown Figure 2.11, represent the condition of the result of an arithmetic or logic operation that has just occurred. In Chapter

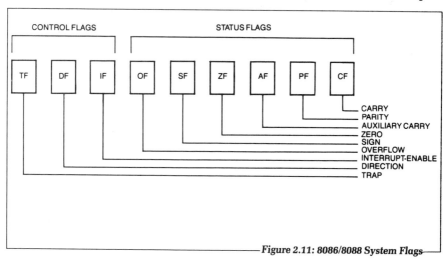

Figure 2.11: 8086/8088 System Flags

4 you will find a group of instructions that will allow the program to alter its execution path, based on the logical value of these flags.

FLAG DEFINITIONS

AF   *auxiliary carry flag* If this flag is set, there has been a carry of the low nibble to the high nibble or a borrow from the high nibble to the low. The high or low nibble refers to the low-order byte of a 16-bit value.

CF   *carry flag* This flag is set when there has been a carry or a borrow to the high-order bit of the (8- or 16-bit) result. (We discussed the general carry flag in Chapter 1.)

OF   *overflow flag* When this flag is set, an arithmetic overflow has occurred. This means that the size of the result exceeded the storage capacity of the destination, and a significant digit has been lost. (The general overflow flag was discussed in Chapter 1.)

SF   *sign flag* This flag is set when the high-order bit of the result is a logical 1. Since negative binary numbers are represented using two's complement notation, SF reflects the sign of the result: a 0 indicates a positive number, and a 1 indicates a negative one.

PF   *parity flag* If this flag is set, the result of the operation has an even number of 1s in it. This flag can be used to check for data transmission errors.

ZF   *zero flag* This flag will be set when the result of the operation is zero.

Figure 2.12 shows the complete set of internal registers for the 8086/8088.

ADDITIONAL CONTROL FLAGS

There are three control flags in the 80866/8 that we have not yet discussed. We have chosen not to cover them at this time because it will be more useful to discuss them when we know more about the 8086/8088 instruction set. These three flags are labeled DF (direction flag), IF (interrupt enable flag) and TF (trap flag).

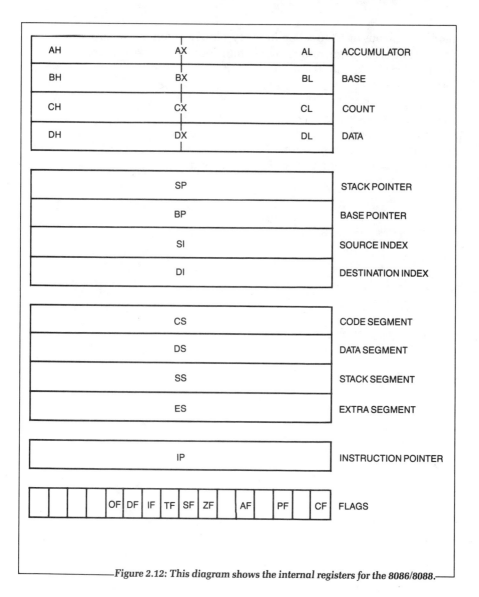

Figure 2.12: This diagram shows the internal registers for the 8086/8088.

SUMMARY

In this chapter we have covered the basic organization of the microprocessor system. We have described ROM, RAM and I/O and have explained how the three bus architecture is interfaced to them. We have defined each bus by its function in the system. In addition, we have examined the internal block diagram of a microprocessor. We have explored each major block, and its interaction with the other blocks. Finally, we have discussed the internal organization of the 8086/8088 beginning with the major blocks of the CPU—the BIU and the EU—and then sharpening our focus to include the internal registers of the 8086/8088.

In the next chapter we will use this information to learn more about the 8086/8088. In particular, we will examine how the 8086/8088 uses the internal registers to form a specific memory address.

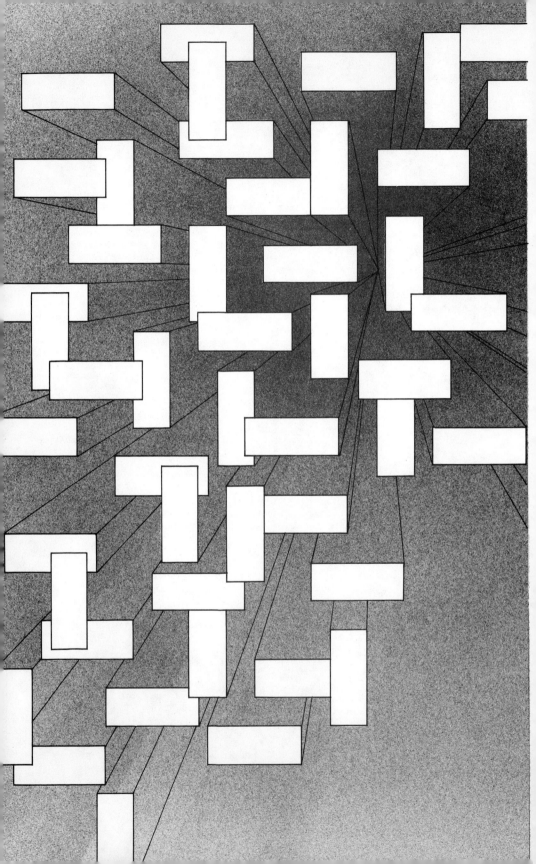

3 8086/8088 MEMORY ORGANIZATION and ADDRESSING MODES

INTRODUCTION

In this chapter we will examine the system memory organizations of the 8086 and 8088 microprocessors. We will point out the many similarities and differences between the two architectures, and we will discuss the different addressing modes for each. We will also look at examples showing how each addressing mode operates. Finally, we will learn how to generate object or binary code for the 8086/8088, and we will discuss several important points regarding the writing of object code.

SYSTEM MEMORY ORGANIZATION OF THE 8086

The 8086 has 20 address lines. This means that it has 2^{20} or 1,048,576 unique storage locations that can be addressed. Since the data bus for the 8086 is 16 bits wide, the system memory for the 8086 is 16 bits (or two bytes) wide. These two bytes are labeled upper byte and lower byte, as shown in Figure 3.1.

The 8086 can access any of the possible 1,048,576 bytes of memory. Since each word of memory uses two bytes, this gives a system memory that is 2^{19} addresses of 16 bits each. (Note: It is important to remember that the 8086 can access bytes of memory, as well as words.)

As we will see in a later chapter, the instructions for the 8086 are made up of 1 to 6 bytes of data. This means that the 8086 instructions may start at either an even (lower byte) or odd (upper byte) address, as shown in Figure 3.2. Two signals determine which byte of memory is being accessed: A0 and BHE.

When A0 is a logical 0, the 8086 is accessing the lower byte of the valid memory address. When BHE is a logical 0, the 8086 is accessing the upper

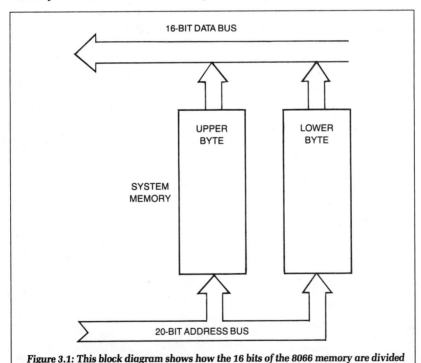

Figure 3.1: *This block diagram shows how the 16 bits of the 8066 memory are divided into upper and lower bytes.*

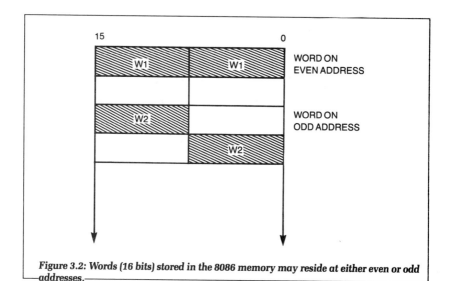

15   0

WORD ON
EVEN ADDRESS

WORD ON
ODD ADDRESS

Figure 3.2: Words (16 bits) stored in the 8086 memory may reside at either even or odd addresses.

byte of the valid memory address. From this, you may be inclined to think that the BHE is simply A0. In some cases, this may be true, but it is not true in all cases.

The 8086 is capable of accessing 16 bits (or two bytes) of data in memory in a single memory cycle. When this occurs, both the BHE and A0 are logical 0 at the same time. As a programmer, you do not need to be aware of these signals; however, it is important that you know that any byte in memory can be accessed separately when certain 8086 instructions are used.

ACCESSING 16 BITS AT AN EVEN ADDRESS

To explain more fully how the 8086 accesses data in memory, let's examine some examples. Let's assume that the 8086 is reading a 16-bit word from address 000F0, an even address. This means that the 8086 requires both the upper and lower byte of data at that address. The CPU then outputs the address on the address bus with BHE and A0 set to a logical 0. Both bytes of data communicate with the CPU at the same time (in a parallel fashion), as seen in Figure 3.3.

ACCESSING 8 BITS AT AN EVEN ADDRESS

Let us now assume that the 8086 is reading a byte from memory address 000F0. Since this address is even, the byte of data will be read from the lower byte of the address data word. In this case, A0 equals logical 0 and BHE equals logical 1.

ACCESSING 8 BITS AT AN ODD ADDRESS

Let's now assume that the 8086 is accessing a byte from address 000F1, an odd address. This data will be read from the upper byte of the 16-bit data word at address 0000F0. In this instance, A0 is a logical 1 and BHE is a logical 0.

ACCESSING 16 BITS AT AN ODD ADDRESS

So far, we have described two cases where the 8086 is accessing data in memory and the logical conditions of A0 and BHE have been different. The following question must now be asked: "What happens if the 8086 accesses a 16-bit word that starts at an odd address?" This problem is shown in Figure 3.4.

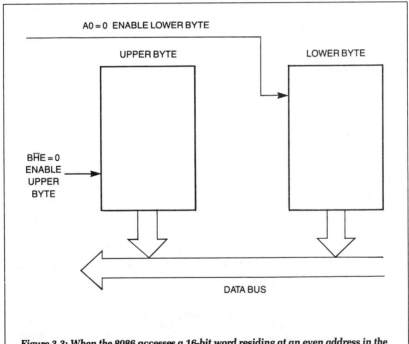

Figure 3.3: When the 8086 accesses a 16-bit word residing at an even address in the system memory, both the upper and lower bytes will be enabled onto the system data bus; and in this case, A0 will equal 0 and BHE will equal 0.

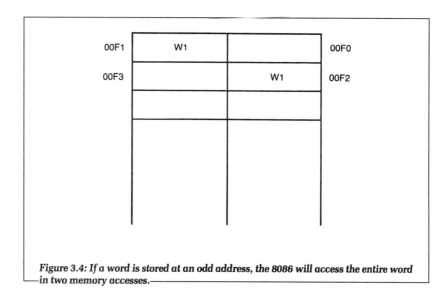

Figure 3.4: If a word is stored at an odd address, the 8086 will access the entire word in two memory accesses.

This is a typical problem due to the flexibility of the memory structure of the 8086. That is, instructions may require an even or odd number of bytes. So that bytes are not wasted, the 8086 allows bytes or words of data to start at either even or odd addresses. Thus, to read a 16-bit word starting at an odd address, the 8086 must perform two memory accesses.

ALIGNED AND NON-ALIGNED WORDS

We now know the different ways that the 8086 accesses data in memory. When the CPU accesses a word (i.e., 16 bits) located on an even address, it is accessing an "aligned" word. The word is aligned because both bytes are located at the same word address and can be read or written in a single memory cycle.

When the CPU accesses a word starting at an odd address, it is said to be accessing a non-aligned word. This is due to the fact that both bytes of the word do not reside at the same word address. Thus, two memory cycles are required to read the entire word. Figure 3.5 shows the concept of aligned and non-aligned words.

The 8086 is designed to handle both aligned and non-aligned words. The importance of words being aligned or non-aligned is determined by the execution speed of certain operations. For example, if your program accesses or manipulates many word quantities, then storing the data starting at an even address can help in the speed of system execution.

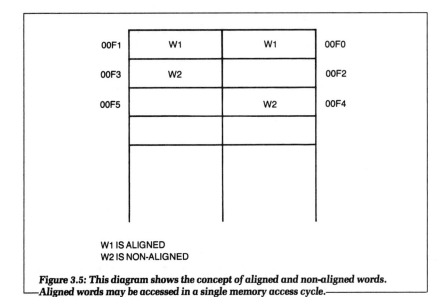

W1 IS ALIGNED
W2 IS NON-ALIGNED

Figure 3.5: This diagram shows the concept of aligned and non-aligned words. Aligned words may be accessed in a single memory access cycle.

SYSTEM MEMORY ORGANIZATION OF THE 8088

Like the 8086 CPU, the 8088 CPU has 20 bits of address. Unlike the 8088, however, it has only an 8-bit data bus. This leads to a memory organization like the one shown in Figure 3.6. The 8088 is essentially an 8-bit system that uses a 16-bit microprocessor. All of the 16-bit software capabilities are available on the 8088. This is demonstrated by the fact that both the 8086 and the 8088 execute the same software instructions.

ADDRESS GENERATION WITH THE 8086/8088

In the preceding discussions we have introduced the memory organization for both the 8086 and the 8088 CPUs. In Chapter 2 we discussed the internal registers for these microprocessors. In the remaining sections of this chapter we will learn how addresses are generated using the internal registers of the CPU. Each different way of generating an address is referred to as an *addressing mode*.

INSTRUCTION ADDRESS GENERATION

Let's first see how the 8086/8088 generates an address for an instruction in memory. Recall from previous discussions that all internal registers on the 8086/8088 are 16 bits wide. However, the physical address bus of the CPU is 20 bits. This means that more than one of the internal registers of the CPU must be used to generate a 20-bit physical address.

The two registers used for the instruction address are the IP (instruction register) and the CS (code segment register). These two registers are combined in a special way to generate a complete 20-bit address. Here is the

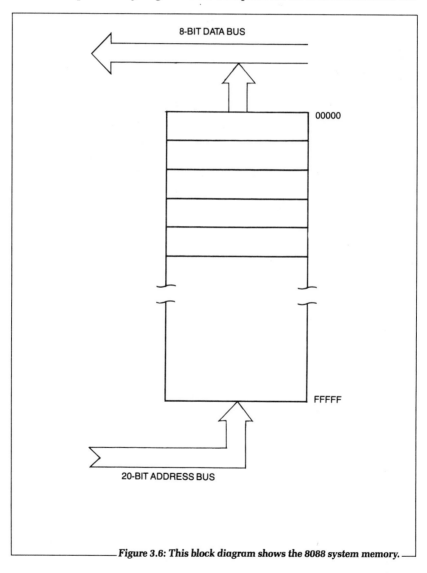

Figure 3.6: This block diagram shows the 8088 system memory.

equation that describes how these two 16-bit registers are combined:

20-bit address = (16 × CS) + IP

For example:

CS register = 1000H
IP register = 0414H

Therefore:

20-bit address = (16 × 1000H)
= 10000H (shifted left 4 bits) + 0414H

This equals

10414H

This is the address in memory from which the new instruction will be fetched. The IP register is referred to as the *offset*—the CS register × 16 points to the starting address or segment in memory from which the offset is computed. That is, it points to the starting address of the *segment* of memory that contains the instruction *codes;* hence, the name *code segment* register. Figure 3.7 displays a block diagram showing how a 20-bit instruction address is computed.

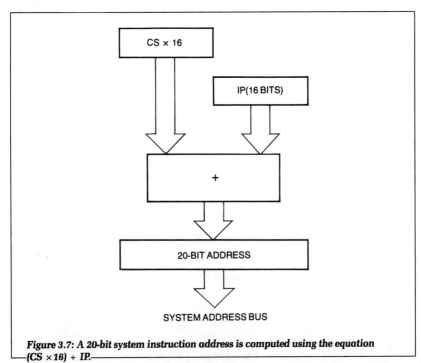

Figure 3.7: A 20-bit system instruction address is computed using the equation (CS × 16) + IP.

Every address generated by the 8086/8088 uses one of the four segment registers. This segment register is then shifted left four bits before it is added to the offset value. The offset value is computed by adding the internal registers. The CPU instruction specifies which internal registers are used to generate the offset. Note that a segment register is never used in the computation of an offset value for address generation.

With this brief introduction to the formation of a 20-bit address, let's examine some examples of the different types of addressing modes used. We will use the 8086/8088 instruction MOV, because it is straightforward to understand. Our goal is to learn more about the different addressing modes of the 8086/8088.

THE MOV INSTRUCTION

The MOV instruction transfers a byte or word from the source operand to the destination operand. (*Note:* an *operand* is data to be operated on by the CPU.) The instruction is written as:

MOV destination, source

IMMEDIATE ADDRESSING

In the immediate addressing mode, the operand appears in the instruction. An example of an immediate instruction is one that moves a constant value into an internal register (which, in this example, is AX):

MOV AX,568

The constant 568 is loaded into the internal register AX. The number 568 will reside in the bytes of memory that comprise the instruction.

REGISTER ADDRESSING

The register addressing mode indicates that the operand to be used is contained in one of the general internal registers of the CPU. In the case of the AX, BX, CX, or DX registers, this register may be 8 or 16 bits. (These registers were discussed in Chapter 2.) For example, the instruction MOV AX,BX will move the contents of the BX register into the AX register. A similiar instruction, MOV AL,BL, will move the contents of the BL register (8 bits) into the AL register. When using register addressing, the CPU performs all operations internally; thus, no 20-bit address is generated to specify the operand.

DIRECT ADDRESSING

The direct addressing mode completely specifies in the instruction, the location in memory that contains the operand. In this type of addressing, a 20-bit address must be formed. This means that some internal address generation on the 8086/8088 will take place. Here is an example of this type of addressing:

MOV CX,COUNT

The value of COUNT is a constant. It is used as the offset value in computing the 20-bit address. The 8086/8088 always uses a segment register when computing a physical address. Which register will be used for this particular instruction? Unless instructed otherwise, the DS or data segment register will be used. (See Figure 3.8.) This is the default segment value. However, any of the four segment values may be used. This is accomplished by specifying the register appropriate in the instruction. For example, suppose we wish to use the ES register, rather than the DS register, we would then specify:

MOV CX,ES:COUNT

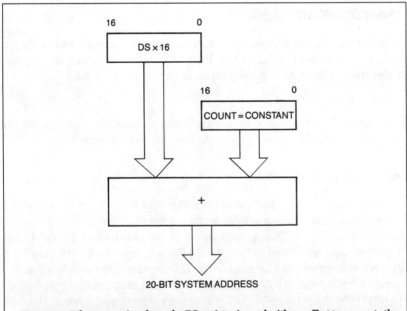

Figure 3.8: When accessing data, the DS register is used with an offset to compute the 20-bit system address. This is the default segment. It can be overriden by using a segment override prefix with an instruction.

where ES is the "segment override prefix" for the instruction. Its value will be used as the segment register for computing the 20-bit physical address.

REGISTER INDIRECT ADDRESSING

With the register index addressing mode, the 16-bit offset address is contained in a base or index register. That is, the address resides in the BX, BP, SI or DI register. Here is an example of this type of addressing:

MOV AX,[SI]

The 16-bit binary value contained in the SI register would be the offset used to compute the 20-bit address. Again, a segment register will be used to generate the final address. The 16-bit value in SI is combined with the proper segment value for address generation.

REGISTER INDIRECT WITH DISPLACEMENT

This type of addressing involves the two previous modes of addressing. The 16-bit offset address is computed by adding the 16-bit value specified by the internal register and a constant. For example, let's use the internal DI register and the constant value (displacement), where COUNT has been previously defined as some number equal to COUNT. The mnemonics for this type of addressing are:

MOV AX, COUNT [DI]

If COUNT = 0378H and DI = 04FAH, then the 16-bit offset address will be 0872H—the sum of 0378H + 04FAH.

REGISTER INDIRECT WITH A BASE AND INDEX REGISTER

This addressing mode uses the sum of two internal registers on the 8086/8088 to obtain the 16-bit offset address to be used in the computation of the 20-bit address. Here are examples of these type of instructions:

A   MOV, [BP] [DI], AX
B   MOV AX, [BX] [SI]

In this instruction, the offset A equals BP + DI and the offset B equals BX + SI.

REGISTER INDIRECT WITH BASE + INDEX + CONSTANT

This is the most complex addressing mode. But if it is taken one piece at a time, it is not too difficult. This addressing mode is identical to the previous addressing mode, except that there is a constant added onto the final 16-bit sum. For example, let's suppose that the following register values are given:

DI   = 0367H
BX   = 7890H
COUNT = 0012H

This addressing mode indicates that the offset specified by the sum of DI + BX + COUNT be used to move the memory data into register AX. The instruction would be written as:

MOV AX, COUNT [BX] [DI]

The 16-bit offset address would be equal to 7C09H, which is the sum of 0367H + 7890H + 0012H. The complete 20-bit address would be computed by the equation (16 × DS) + 7C09H. If the DS register equals 3000H, then the complete, physical 20-bit address would equal (16 × 3000H) + 7C09H = 37C09H.

8086/8088 OBJECT CODE

The preceding addressing modes are used by the 8086/8088. As a programmer, you will write the mnemonics. The object code is very often generated by the computer. (Recall that the *object code* is the actual data bytes that the CPU executes.) In the remainder of this chapter we will discuss the details of how the object code is generated for the 8086/8088 CPU. This information will help you in your study of the 8086/8088 instruction set (given in Chapter 4).

We will now discuss the important points of generating the object code for the 8086/8088. Let's examine some examples. These examples are the same ones that we presented earlier, in the addressing mode sections. In each case we will present the object code and an explanation of why the bits are set to a logical 1 or a logical 0.

Before we examine any object code examples, we should explain that it is difficult to say exactly how many bytes a certain instruction will require. (Those who have previously programmed 8-bit microprocessors will recall that this has not always been the case.) With the 8086/8088 instruction set, each type of addressing mode may require a different number of data bytes. Therefore, in the examples that follow we will provide the number of bytes required for each addressing mode for a particular instruction. Your job will be to decide what the data in each byte must be. This task will become more clear to you as we proceed in the discussion.

REG FIELD AND W BIT

The first example we will discuss is the instruction MOV AX,568. This instruction indicates an immediate move to an internal register. The internal register is the destination. It can be a byte or a word register. This instruction requires 2 or 3 bytes, as shown in Figure 3.9.

We can see in this figure that the first byte of data for this instruction has the upper 4 bits as 1011. The next bit is W. The W is for WORD = 1 or BYTE = 0. That is, if the destination register is a 16-bit or word register, then this bit is a logical 1. If the destination register is an 8-bit or byte register, then this bit is a logical 0.

The next three bits of the first byte shown in Figure 3.9 are labeled REG. This 3-bit field determines which register, byte, or word the data will be input to. The 3-bit definitions for the registers are shown in Figure 3.10.

1011W REG	DATA	DATA IF W = 1

Figure 3.9: This figure shows object code for the MOV reg,constant instruction.

	16-BIT REGISTER	8-BIT REGISTER
000	AX	AL
001	CX	CL
010	DX	DL
011	BX	BL
100	SP	AH
101	BP	CH
110	SI	DH
111	DI	BH

Figure 3.10: This figure gives the register definitions (8- and 16-bit) for the object code REG field.

Examining the next two bytes of the instruction in Figure 3.9, we can see that they are labeled DATA. If the destination register is a byte, then the data will be in the second byte of the instruction. If the destination is a word, then the second byte of the instruction will be the lower byte of the 16-bit immediate data. The third byte of the instruction will be the upper byte of the 16-bit immediate data.

For this example (MOV AX,568) we will assume that the 568 is a hexadecimal immediate data. We will also assume that the instruction is a 3-byte one, and that the bytes are B8 68 05. Notice that the first byte has the W bit equal to 1 and the REG equal to 000 for AX.

However, if the instruction had been MOV AL,56, the instruction would then be two bytes. These bytes would be B0 56. The first byte would have the W bit equal to 0 and the register equal to 000 for AL, as shown in Figure 3.10.

D BIT, MOD, AND R/M

In this example, we will move data *from* memory, or move a register *to* or *from* a register. We will use an instruction like MOV AX,BX. This instruction is 2 bytes because there is no memory address to add on. The bytes will appear as shown in Figure 3.11.

We can see in Figure 3.11 that the first byte has the lower two bits as DW. The W is for word or byte (as shown previously). The D is to indicate if the data is to be stored in the operand specified by the MOD and R/M field, D = 0, or if it is to be stored in the register specified by the REG field, D = 1.

Figure 3.12 shows the MOD and R/M assignments. Notice in the MOD description that if the value is 11, then the R/M field is encoded with a register format. This format was shown in Figure 3.10.

For this instruction we wish to store the data in the AX register. Therefore, the D bit will be a logical 0. This means that the data must be stored in the location specified by the MOD and R/M fields. Therefore, the MOD will equal 11. The R/M field will equal 000, indicating that the AX register is the destination for the data. The REG field for the second byte of data will equal 011, thus indicating that the BX register is the source register to

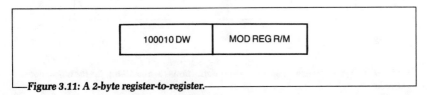

Figure 3.11: A 2-byte register-to-register.

be used (this value comes from Figure 3.10). The complete second byte of data for the instruction will be 11 011 000 or D8. Thus, the object code for the instruction MOV AX,BX is 89D8.

BASE AND INDEX REGISTER SPECIFIED
BY R/M FOR OPERANDS IN MEMORY (MOD≠ 11)

R/M FIELD	BASE REGISTER	INDEX REGISTER
000	BX	SI
001	BX	DI
010	BP	SI
011	BP	DI
100	NONE	SI
101	NONE	DI
110	BP	NONE
111	BX	NONE

MOD	DISPLACEMENT	COMMENT
00	ZERO	
01	8-BIT CONTENTS OF NEXT BYTE OF INSTRUCTION SIGN EXTENDED TO 16 BITS	INSTRUCTION CONTAINS AN ADDITIONAL BYTE
10	16-BIT CONTENTS OF NEXT TWO BYTES OF INSTRUCTION	INSTRUCTION CONTAINS TWO ADDITIONAL BYTES
11	R/M REGISTER	

IF MOD = 00 AND R/M = 110, THEN:
1. THE ABOVE DOES NOT APPLY
2. THE INSTRUCTION CONTAINS TWO ADDITIONAL BYTES
3. THE OFFSET ADDRESS IS CONTAINED IN THOSE BYTES

Figure 3.12: R/M field and MOD definitions for the 8086/8088 object code.

OBJECT CODE FOR INDEXING
AND BASE REGISTER USE

Let us examine one last example of generating object code for the 8086/8088. In this example we will calculate the object code for the instruction MOV BX, COUNT [BX] [SI]. This instruction has the same general format as the previous example. The byte count for this instruction is 4. These bytes are shown in Figure 3.13.

The first byte of Figure 3.13 will have the D bit set to a logical 1. This is due to the fact that the destination for the data will be specified by the REG field in the second byte. The W bit will be set to a logical 1 because it is a word transfer. This gives a first byte data equal to 10001011 or 8B.

Next, we go to the MOD field of the second byte. Since we are using a constant that requires 16 bits, the MOD will be set to 10. Referring to Figure 3.12 this indicates that the displacement will be formatted in two bytes and will follow this byte.

The next field for the second byte is the register field or REG. Since we will be using the CX register, this value will be set to 001 (this was obtained from the register field definitions given in Figure 3.10).

Finally, we have the R/M field. Since the MOD field was not equal to 11, this field will specify which base and index registers are being used to generate the 16-bit offset address. In our case, we are using the (BX + SI + DISP) field. This corresponds to a R/M of 000. See Figure 3.12.

The total second byte of data will be equal to 10 001 000. This is equal to 88. The third and fourth bytes will be equal to the displacement. In this case, the value of count will be equal to 0345 in hexadecimal. The last two bytes will be 4503. This gives a total object code for the instruction MOV CX, COUNT [BX] [SI] = 8B 88 45 03.

OBJECT CODE SUMMARY

One question you may be asking at this point is "Will I have to figure out the D, W, REG, MOD and R/M fields all the time?" If this were the case, then you probably would not program the 8086/8088. Fortunately, your

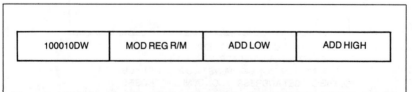

| 100010DW | MOD REG R/M | ADD LOW | ADD HIGH |

Figure 3.13: The object code format for an instruction like MOV BX, COUNT [BX] [SI].

computer will help you figure them out. This object code section has been presented only to enable you to better understand the inner workings of the 8086/8088 microprocessors.

SUMMARY

In this chapter we have discussed some important topics relating to programming the 8086/8088 microprocessors. We started with a presentation of the organization of the system memory for both CPUs. This discussion was provided to help you more clearly understand how the instructions are organized in the system memory; furthermore, it allows you to see the differences and similarities between the 8086/8088 systems.

Next we discussed all the addressing modes. As each mode was presented, examples were given to show exactly how the addresses were generated. We also discussed the segment, base and index registers, and learned how a physical 20-bit system address is internally generated by the CPU.

We ended the chapter with examples showing how to generate object codes for the 8086/8088. These examples included discussions of the different fields that make up the object code, including the D, W, R/M, REG, and MOD fields.

The information given in this chapter should help you to better understand the encoding of the instructions shown in the next chapter.

4 THE INSTRUCTION SET: INDIVIDUAL DESCRIPTIONS

In this chapter we will present the complete 8086/8088 instruction set, listed alphabetically by mnemonics. We will give a brief description of each instruction and show the use of each instruction in assembly language (with arguments included). In addition, we will describe how the 8086/8088 executes each instruction. This is helpful if you want a quick reference displaying what actually occurs during the execution of an instruction. Each description will include any special considerations that a particular instruction might have, and it will detail when each instruction can and cannot be used.

For certain instructions we will give examples. For others it will be clear from the descriptions exactly how they are to be used.

Finally, we will show the object code for each instruction.

The mnemonics used in this chapter are consistent with those designed by Intel Corporation. The information presented should not only help you better understand how the 8086/8088 microprocessor can be programmed, but it should also serve as a valuable reference when you actually begin writing programs in assembly language.

The table below shows the abbreviations and symbols, and Figure 4.1 shows the 8086/8088 register model that we will use in the descriptions that follow of the 8086/8088 instructions.

ABBREVIATIONS AND SYMBOLS
FOR INSTRUCTION DESCRIPTIONS

If d = 1, then "to"; if d = 0, then "from"

If w = 1, then word instruction; if w = 0, then byte instruction

If s:w = 01, then 16 bits of immediate data form the operand

If s:w = 11, then an immediate data byte is sign-extended to form the 16-bit operand

If v = 0, then "count" = 1; if v = 1, then "count" in CL

x = don't care

z is used for some string instructions to compare with the ZF flag.

AL = 8-bit accumulator

AX = 16-bit accumulator

CX = Count register

DX = Variable port register

DS = Data Segment

ES = Extra Segment

Above/below refers to unsigned value

Greater = more positive

Less = less positive (more negative) signed values

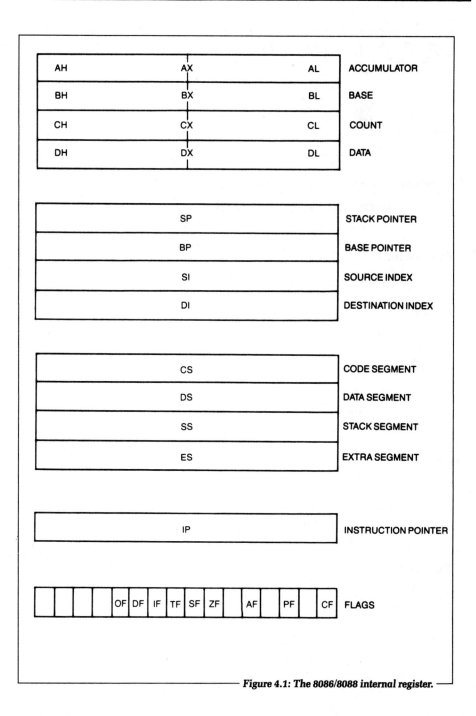

Figure 4.1: The 8086/8088 internal register.

| **AAA** | — *ASCII Adjust for Addition* ——————— |

Mnemonic:

AAA no operands

Function:

If D3, D2, D1, D0 of AL > 9 or AF flag = 1, then AL = AL + 6, AH = AH + 1, AF = 1, CF = AF, AL = AL "and" 0Fh

Flags Defined:

AF, CF

Flags Undefined:

OF, PF, SF, ZF

Description:

The AAA instruction changes the value of the AL register to a valid unpacked decimal number; bits D7–D4 of the AL register are zeroed.

Example:

AAA

Before:	*After:*
AL = 0Bh	AL = 01h
AH = 00h	AH = 01h

Encoding:

00110111

——————————— *ASCII Adjust for Division* — | **AAD** |—

Mnemonic:

AAD no operands

Function:

AL = ((AH * 0Ah) + AL; AH = 0)

Flags Defined:

PF, SF, ZF

Flags Undefined:

AF, CF, OF

Description:

The AAD instruction changes the contents of the AL and AH registers (each containing a valid unpacked BCD number) to an equivalent binary number contained in the AL register. This enables the programmer to use the IDIV instruction to produce the correct result. The AH register must be zero prior to the IDIV instruction. After the IDIV instruction, the quotient is returned in AL and the remainder is returned in AH. Both high-order half-bytes are zeroed.

Example:

AAD

Before:	*After:*
AL = 03h	AL = 35h
AH = 05h	AH = 00h

Encoding:

11010101	00001010

All mnemonics copyright Intel Corporation, 1981.

AAM — *ASCII Adjust for Multiply* ⸺

Mnemonic:

AAM no operands

Function:

AH = AL / 0Ah; AL = remainder

Flags Defined:

PF, SF, ZF

Flags Undefined:

AF, CF, OF

Description:

The AAM instruction corrects the result of a multiplication of two valid unpacked BCD numbers. A valid unpacked BCD number is formed from the content of AH and AL. The binary number in AL is divided by 10 and the quotient is stored into the AH register. The remainder from the division is stored in the AL register. The high-order half-bytes of the multiplied operands must have been 0h in order for AAM to produce a correct result.

Example:

AAM

Before:	*After:*
AH = 00h	AH = 06h
AL = 41h	AL = 05h

Encoding:

11010100	00001010

———————— *ASCII Adjust for Subtraction* — $\boxed{\textbf{AAS}}$ —

Mnemonic:

AAS no operands

Function:

If D3, D2, D1, D0 of AL > 9 or AF flag = 1, then AL = AL − 6, AH = AH − 1, AF = 1, CF = AF, AL = AL "and" 0Fh

Flags Defined:

AF, CF

Flags Undefined:

OF, PF, SF, ZF

Description:

AAS corrects the result of a previous subtraction of two valid unpacked decimal operands. AAS changes the content of AL to a valid unpacked decimal number. The high-order half-byte is zeroed.

Encoding:

00111111

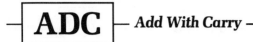

ADC — *Add With Carry*

Mnemonic:

ADC destination, source

Function:

If CF = 1 then destination = destination + source + 1
If CF = 0 then destination = destination + source

Flags Defined:

AF, CF, OF, PF, SF, ZF

Description:

ADC sums the operands, which may be bytes or words, and then adds one if CF is set and replaces the destination operand with the result. Both operands may be signed or unsigned binary numbers.

Example:

ADC AX,BX
ADC AL,9
ADC BX,458

Encoding:

Memory or Register Operand with Register Operand

000100dw	mod reg r/m

Immediate Operand to Memory or Register Operand

100000sw	mod 010 r/m	data	data if s:w = 01

Immediate Operand to Accumulator

0001010w	data	data if w = 1

Addition — ADD

Mnemonic:

ADD destination, source

Function:

destination = destination + source

Flags Defined:

AF, CF, OF, PF, SF, ZF

Description:

The sum of the two operands, which may be bytes or words, replaces the destination operand.

Example:

ADD DX,CX
ADD AX,400
ADD label,BL

Encoding:

Memory or Register Operand with Register Operand

000000dw	mod reg r/m

Immediate Operand to Memory or Register Operand

100000sw	mod 000 r/m	data	data if s:w = 01

Immediate Operand to Accumulator

0000010w	data	data if w = 1

All mnemonics copyright Intel Corporation, 1981.

AND — And Logical

Mnemonic:

AND destination, source

Function:

destination = destination "and" source
CF = 0, OF = 0

Flags Defined:

CF, OF, PF, SF, ZF

Flags Undefined:

AF

Description:

AND performs the logical "and" of the two operands (byte or word) and returns the result to the destination operand. A bit in the result is set to a logical 1 if both bits of the original operands are a logical 1; otherwise, the bit is cleared.

Example:

AND BX,CX

Before:	After:
BX = AC07h	BX = 2004h
CX = 23F4h	CX = 23F4h

Encoding:

Memory or Register Operand with Register Operand

001000dw	mod reg r/m

Immediate Operand to Memory or Register Operand

| 1000000w | mod 100 r/m | data | data if w = 1 |

Immediate Operand to Accumulator

| 0010010w | data | data if w = 1 |

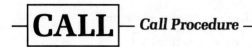

CALL — *Call Procedure*

Mnemonic:

CALL Procedure-name

Function:

If inter-segment then: SP = SP – 2;   CS pushed
 CS = new segment specified: SP = SP – 2;   IP pushed
 IP = new instruction pointer specified

If intra-segment, then: SP = SP – 2;   IP pushed
 IP = new instruction pointer specified

Flags Affected:

Description:

CALL activates an out-of-line procedure, saving information on the stack to permit a RET (return) instruction in the procedure to transfer control back to the instruction following the CALL. The assembler generates a different type of CALL instruction depending on whether the programmer has defined the procedure name as NEAR or FAR. For control to return properly, the type of CALL instruction must match the type of return (RET) instruction that exists from the procedure.

For an intra-segment direct CALL, SP is decremented by two and IP is pushed onto the stack. The target procedure's relative displacement (up to ± 32K) from the CALL instruction is then added to the instruction pointer.

An intra-segment indirect CALL may be made through memory or a register. SP is decremented by two and the IP is pushed onto the stack. The target procedure offset is obtained from the memory word or 16-bit general register referenced in the instruction that replaces the IP.

All mnemonics copyright Intel Corporation, 1981.

For an inter-segment direct CALL, SP is decremented by two, and CS is pushed onto the stack. CS is replaced by the segment word contained in the instruction. SP is again decremented by two, and the IP is pushed onto the stack and replaced by the offset word in the instruction.

For an inter-segment indirect CALL, SP is decremented by two, and CS is pushed onto the stack. CS is then replaced by the content of the second word of the double-word memory pointer referenced by the instruction. SP is again decremented by two, and IP is pushed onto the stack and replaced by the contents of the first word or the double-word pointer referenced by the instruction.

Example:

CALL NEAR
CALL FAR
CALL AX

Encoding:

Intra-Segment Direct

11101000	disp-low	disp-high

Destination = Effective Address

Intra-Segment Indirect

11111111	mod 010 r/m

Destination = IP + displacement

Inter-Segment Direct

10011010	offset-low	offset-high	seg-low	seg-high

Destination = offset, SEGMENT = Segment

Inter-Segment Indirect

11111111	mod 011 r/m

Destination = Effective address, Segment = Effective address + 2

CBW — *Convert Byte to Word*

Mnemonic:

CBW no operands

Function:

If AL < 80h then AH = 00h
If AL > 80h then AH = FFh

Flags Affected:

Description:

CBW extends the sign of the byte in register AL through register AH.

Example:

CBW

Before: After:
AL = 83h   AH = FFh: AL = 83h
AL = 56h   AH = 00h: AL = 56h

Encoding:

```
10011000
```

Clear Carry — **CLC**

Mnemonic:

CLC no operands

Function:

CF = 0

Flags Defined:

CF

Description:

CLC zeroes the carry flag (CF) and affects no other flags.

Encoding:

11111000

CLD — *Clear Direction Flag* —————————

Mnemonic:

CLD no operands

Function:

DF = 0

Flags Defined:

DF

Description:

CLD zeroes DF, causing the string instructions to auto-increment the SI and/or DI index registers.

Encoding:

11111100

Clear Interrupt Enable Flag — CLI —

Mnemonic:

> CLI

Function:

> IF = 0

Flags Defined

> IF

Description:

> CLI zeroes the IF flag, which will disable maskable interrupts. Software interrupts are not disabled.

Encoding:

> | 11111010 |
> | --- |

CMC — *Complement Carry Flag*

Mnemonic:

CMC no operands

Function:

If CF = 0 then CF = 1; if CF = 1 then CF = 0

Flags Defined:

CF

Description:

CMC "toggles" CF to its opposite state.

Encoding:

11110101

Compare —  |—

Mnemonic:

CMP destination, source

Function:

destination − source

Flags Defined:

AF, CF, OF, PF, SF, ZF

Description:

CMP subtracts the source from the destination, which may be bytes or words, but does not return the result. The operands are unchanged, but the flags are updated and can be tested by a subsequent conditional jump instruction.

Example:

CMP DX,CX
CMP AL,25
CMP BH,Label

Encoding:

Memory or register Operand with Register Operand

001110dw	mod reg r/m

Immediate Operand to Memory or Register Operand

100000sw	mod 111 r/m	data	data if s:w = 01

Immediate Operand with Accumulator

0011110w	data	data if w = 1

All mnemonics copyright Intel Corporation, 1981.

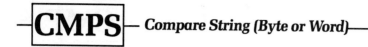

CMPS — Compare String (Byte or Word)

Mnemonic:

CMPS (destination-string) – (source-string)

Function:

(destination-string) – (source-string)
If DF = 0, then SI = SI + delta, DI = DI + delta
If DF = 1, then SI = S – delta, DI = DI – delta

If string is byte then delta is 1
If string is word then delta is 2

Destination string is addressed by DI
Source string is addressed by SI

Flags Defined:

F, CF, OF, PF, SF, ZF

Description:

CMPS (Compare String) subtracts the destination byte or word (addressed by DI) from the source byte or word (addressed by SI). CMPS affects the flags but does not alter either operand. If CMPS is prefixed with REPE or REPZ, the operation is interpreted as "compare while not end-of-string (CX not zero) and the strings are equal (ZF = 1)." If CMPS is preceded by REPNE or REPNZ, the operation is interpreted "as compare while not end-of-string (CX not zero) and the strings are not equal (ZF = 0)." Thus, CMPS can be used to find matching or differing string elements.

The operands named in the CMPS instruction are used only by the assembler to verify type and accessibility using current segment register contents.

Encoding:

```
1010011w
```

All mnemonics copyright Intel Corporation, 1981.

---------------- *Convert Word to Double Word* — | **CWD** |-

Mnemonic:

CWD no operands

Function:

If AX < 8000h then DX = 0
If AX > 8000h then DX = FFFFh

Flags Affected:

Description:

CWD extends the sign of the word register AX throughout register DX.

Example:

CWD

Before:	*After:*
AX = 9034h	DX = FFFFh, AX = 9034h
AX = 7034h	DX = FFFFh, AX = 7034h

Encoding:

10011001

DAA — *Decimal Adjust for Addition*

Mnemonic:

DAA no operands

Function:

If D3, D2, D1, D0 of AL > 9 or AF flag = 1,
  then AL = AL + 6: AF = 1
If AL > 9Fh or CF flag = 1,
  then AL = AL + 60h: CF = 1

Flags Defined:

AF, CR, PF, SF, ZF

Flags Undefined:

OF

Description:

DAA changes the content of AL to a pair of valid packed decimal digits.

Example:

DAA

Before: *After:*
AL 8Ah   AL = 90h

Encoding:

00100111

———————— *Decimal Adjust for Subtraction* — $\boxed{\textbf{DAS}}$ —

Mnemonic:

DAS no operands

Function:

If D3, D2, D1, D0 of AL > 9 or AF = 1
   then AL = AL − 6; F = 1
If AL > 9Fh or CF = 1 then AL = AL − 60h; CF = 1

Flags Defined:

AF, CR, PF, SF, ZF

Flag Undefined:

OF

Description:

DAS changes the content of AL to a pair of valid packed decimal digits that were the result of a previous subtraction.

Example:

DAS

Before: *After:*
AL = 1Fh   AL = 19h

Encoding:

00101111

DEC —Decrement

Mnemonic:

DEC destination

Function:

destination = destination − 1

Flag Defined:

AF, OF, PF, SF, ZF

Description:

DEC subtracts one from the destination operand. The operand may be a byte or a word.

Example:

DEC BX

Before:	After:
BX = 12h	11FFh

Encoding:

Memory or Register Operand

1111111w	mod 001 r/m

Register Operand

01001reg

—Divide—  **DIV**

Mnemonic:

DIV source

Function:

If source operand = byte: AX / source: AH = Quotient
AL = remainder
If source operand = word: AX, DX / source, AX = Quotient,
DX = remainder, where contains the most-significant 16 bits
for the divide.

Flags Defined:

Flags Undefined:

AF, CF, OF, PF, SF, ZF

Description:

DIV (divide) performs an unsigned division of the accumulator
(and its extension) by the source operand. If the source operand is
a byte, it is divided into the double-length dividend assumed to be
in registers AL and AH. The single-length remainder is returned
in AH. If the source operand is a word, it is divided into the
double-length dividend in registers AX and DX. The single-length
remainder is returned in DX. If the quotient exceeds the capacity
of its destination register (FFH for byte source, FFFFH for word
source), as when division by zero is attempted, a type 0 interrupt
is generated. At this time the quotient and remainder are undefined. Non-integral quotients are truncated to integers.

Example:

DIV 25 this is a byte

Before:	*After:*
AH = 00h	AH = 01h remainder
AL = 33h	AL = 02h quotient

DIV 300 this is a word

Before:	*After:*
DX = 0000h	DX = 0005h remainder
AX = 0389h	AX = 0003h quotient
DIV CL	
DIV CX	

Encoding:

1111011w	mod 110 r/m	2–4 bytes may follow

Escape— **ESC**

Mnemonic:

ESC external opcode, address

Function:

If MOD is not equal to 11, the instruction is placed on the data bus.
If MOD is equal to 11, a no-operation is performed.

Flags Affected:

None

Description:

The Escape instruction provides a mechanism by which other processors (co-processors) may receive their instructions from the 8086/8088 instruction stream and make use of the 8086/8088 addressing modes. The CPU does no operation for the ESC instruction other than to access memory and place the operand on the data bus. The 8086/8088 are designed to operate with a variety of co-processors that perform different system functions. Two co-processors that operate with the 8086/8088 are the 8089 Input and Output Processor and the 8087 Numeric data processor.

Example:

ESC 6, AL

Encoding:

11011xxx	mod xxx r/m

Mnemonic:

HLT no operands

Function:

None

Flags Affected:

None

Description:

HLT causes the 8086/8088 to enter the halt state. The processor leaves the halt state upon activation of the RESET line, upon receipt of a non-maskable interrupt request on NMI, or, if interrupts are enabled, upon receipt of a maskable interrupt request on INTR.

Encoding:

11110100

Integer Divide 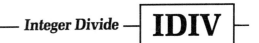 IDIV

Mnemonic:

IDIV source

Function:

If it is a byte source, the quotient is returned in AL, the remainder is returned in AH, and the dividend is contained in AX and is divided by the source specified.

If it is a word source, the quotient is returned in AX, the remainder is returned in DX, and the dividend is contained in AX, DX and is divided by the source specified.

Flags Defined:

None

Flags Undefined:

AF, CF, OF, PF, SF, ZF

Description:

Integer Divide performs a signed division of the accumulator (and its extension) by the source operand. If the source operand is a byte, it is divided into the double-length dividend assumed to be in registers AL and AH. The single-length quotient is returned in AL, and the single-length remainder is returned in AH. For byte integer division, the maximum positive quotient is + 127 (7FH) and the minimum negative quotient is – 127 (81H). If the source operand is a word, it is divided into the double-length dividend in registers AX and DX. The single-length quotient is returned in AX, and the single-length remainder is returned in DX. For word integer division, the maximum positive quotient is + 2,767 (7FFFH) and the minimum negative quotient is – 32,767 (8001H).

If the quotient is positive and exceeds the maximum, or is negative and is less than the minimum, the quotient and remainder are undefined, and a type 0 interrupt is generated. Non-integral quotients are truncated (towards 0) to integers, and the remainder has the same sign as the dividend.

Example:

    IDIV CL
    IDIV BX

Encoding:

1111011w	mod 111 r/m

Integer Multiply —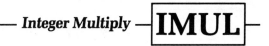

Mnemonic:

> IMUL source

Function:

> If byte source: AX = AL × source (signed)
> If word source: AX, DX = AX × source (signed)

Flags Defined:

> CF, OF

Flags Undefined:

> AF, PF, SF, ZF

Description:

> IMUL performs a signed multiplication of the source operand and the accumulator. If the source is a byte, then it is multiplied by register AL, and the double-length result is returned in AH and AL. If the source is a word, then it is multiplied by register AX, and the double-length result is returned in registers DX and AX. If the upper-half of the result (AH for byte source, DX for word source) is not the sign extension of the lower-half of the result, CF and OF are set; otherwise, they are cleared. When CF and OF are set, they indicate that AH or DX contains significant digits of the result.

Example:

> IMUL BL
> IMUL CL
> IMUL 400

Encoding:

1111011w	mod 101 r/m

All mnemonics copyright Intel Corporation, 1981.

IN	— *Input Byte Or Word* ———————————————

Mnemonic:

IN accumulator, port

Function:

If byte: AL = data from port number, or AL = data addressed by DX register.

If word: AX = data from port number, or AX = data addressed by DX register.

Flags Affected:

None

Description:

IN transfers a byte or a word from an input port to the AL or AX register, respectively. The port number may be specified either with an immediate byte constant, 0 – 255, or with a number previously placed in the DX register, 0 – 65,535.

Example:

IN AL,045H	immediate byte
IN AX,046H	immediate word
IN AL,DX	byte variable port
IN AX,DX	word variable port

Encoding:

Fixed Port

1110010w	port

Variable Port

1110110w	port address is contained in DX register

All mnemonics copyright Intel Corporation, 1981.

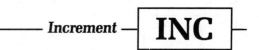

Increment — **INC**

Mnemonic:

INC destination

Function:

Destination = Destination + 1

Flags Defined:

AF, OF, PF, SF, ZF

Description:

INC adds 1 to the destination operand. The operand may be a byte or a word.

Example:

INC BL
INC BX

Encoding:

Memory or Register Operand

1111111w	mod 000 r/m

Register Operand

01000reg

INT — Interrupt

Mnemonic:

INT interrupt type 0 – 255

Function:

SP = SP – 2; Flags pushed; IF = 0; TF = 0; SP = SP – 2; CS pushed;

New CS = data at memory address (type $*$ 4 + 2); SP = SP – 2; IP pushed;

New IP = data at memory address type $*$ 4.

Flags Defined:

TF, IF

Description:

INT activates the interrupt procedure specified by the interrupt-type operand. The address of the interrupt pointer is calculated by multiplying the interrupt-type by 4. The second word of the interrupt pointer replaces CS. The first word of the interrupt pointer replaces IP.

If the type is specified as 3, the assembler will generate a special one-byte form of the interrupt instruction. This is the breakpoint interrupt.

Example:

INT 3
INT 58

Encoding:

| 1100110v | type if v = 1 |

If v = 0, then type = 3

Interrupt On Overflow — **INTO**

Mnemonic:

INTO no operands

Function:

If OF = 1 then: SP = SP – 2; Flags are pushed; IF = 0; TF = 0;
SP = SP – 2; CS is pushed; New CS = data at memory location 12H;
SP = SP – 2; IP is pushed; New IP = data at memory location 10H.

Flags Affected:

None

Description:

INTO generates a software interrupt if the overflow flag (OF) is set; otherwise, control proceeds to the following instruction without activating an interrupt procedure.

Encoding:

11001110

 — *Interrupt On Return* ——————————

Mnemonic:

IRET no operands

Function:

IP popped from stack: SP = SP + 2; CS is popped from the stack; SP = SP + 2; Flags popped from the stack; SP = SP + 2.

Flags Defined:

ALL

Description:

IRET transfers control back to the point of interruption by popping IP, CS, and the flags from the stack. IRET is used to exit any interrupt procedure, whether activated by hardware or software.

Encoding:

11001111

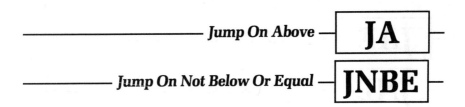

Jump On Above — **JA**

Jump On Not Below Or Equal — **JNBE**

Mnemonic:

JA   8-bit signed displacement
JNBE   8-bit signed displacement

Function:

If CF and ZF = 0, then IP = IP + 8-bit displacement.
Displacement is sign-extended to 16 bits.

Flags Affected:

None

Description:

JA and JNBE transfer control to the target operand (IP + displacement) under the conditions CF and ZF = 0 (or false). Both of these mnemonics will generate the same instruction code by the assembler.

Example:

JA   label
JNBE   label

Encoding:

01110111	disp

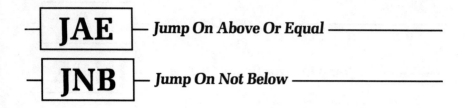

JAE — *Jump On Above Or Equal*

JNB — *Jump On Not Below*

Mnemonic:

> JAE 8-bit signed displacement
> JNB 8-bit signed displacement

Function:

> If CF = 0, then IP = IP + displacement (sign-extended to 16 bits).

Flags Affected:

> None

Description:

> JAE and JNB transfer control to the target operand (IP + displacement) if the condition (CF = 0) is above or equal/not below the tested value. Both of these mnemonics will generate the same instruction code for the 8086/8088.

Example:

> JAE label
> JNB label

Encoding:

01110011	disp

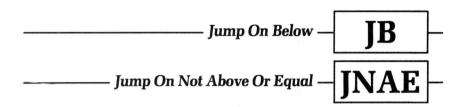

Jump On Below — **JB**

Jump On Not Above Or Equal — **JNAE**

Mnemonic:

JB   8-bit signed displacement
JNAE 8-bit signed displacement

Function:

If CF = 1, then IP = IP + displacement (sign-extended to 16 bits).

Flags Affected:

None

Description:

JB and JNAE transfer control to the target operand (IP + displacement) if the condition (CF = 1) is below/not above or equal to the tested value. Both of these mnemonics will generate the same instruction for the 8086/8088.

Example:

JB   label
JNAE label

Encoding:

01110010	disp

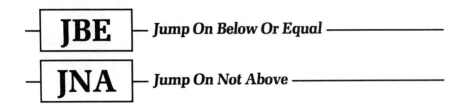

JBE — *Jump On Below Or Equal* —————————

JNA — *Jump On Not Above* —————————

Mnemonic:

JBE   8-bit signed label
JNA   8-bit signed label

Function:

If CF or ZF = 1, then IP = IP + 8-bit signed label (sign-extended to 16 bits).

Flags Affected:

None

Description:

JBE and JNA transfer control to the target operand (IP + displacement) if the conditions (CF or ZF = 1) are below or equal/or not above the tested value. These two mnemonics will generate the same instruction for the 8086/8088.

Example:

JBE   label
JNA   label

Encoding:

01110110	disp

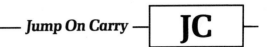

Jump On Carry — **JC**

Mnemonic:

JC 8-bit signed label

Function:

If CF = 1, then IP = IP + 8-bit signed label (sign-extended to 16 bits).

Flags Affected:

None

Description:

JC transfers control to the target operand (IP + displacement) if CF = 1.

Example:

JC label

Encoding:

01110010	disp

Mnemonic:

JCXZ 8-bit signed label

Function:

If CX = 0, then IP = IP + displacement (sign-extended to 16 bits).

Flags Affected:

None

Description:

JCXZ transfers control to the target operand if CX is 0. This instruction is useful at the beginning of a loop to bypass the loop if CX has a zero value (that is, to execute the loop zero times).

Example:

JCXZ label

Encoding:

11100011	disp

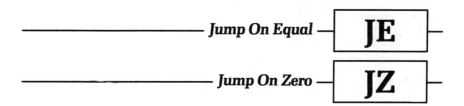

Jump On Equal — **JE**

Jump On Zero — **JZ**

Mnemonic:

JE 8-bit signed label
JZ 8-bit signed label

Function:

If ZF = 1, then IP = IP + displacement (sign-extended to 16 bits).

Flags Affected:

None

Description:

JE and JZ transfer control to the target operand (IP + displacement) if the condition (ZF = 1) is equal/or zero on the tested value. Both of these mnemonics will generate the same instruction for the 8086/8088.

Example:

JE label
JZ label

Encoding:

01110100	disp

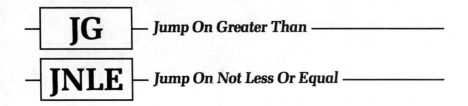

Mnemonic:

> JG   8-bit signed label
> JNLE 8-bit signed label

Function:

> If SF = OF and ZF = 0, then IP = IP + displacement (sign-extended to 16 bits).

Flags Affected:

> None

Description:

> JG and JNLE transfer control to the target operand (IP + displacement) if the condition SF xor OF = 0 or ZF = 0 is greater than/not less than or equal to the tested value. Both of these mnemonics will generate the same instruction for the 8086/8088.

Example:

> JG   label
> JNLE label

Encoding:

01111111	disp

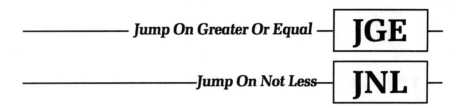

Jump On Greater Or Equal — **JGE**

Jump On Not Less — **JNL**

Mnemonic:

JGE 8-bit signed displacement
JNL 8-bit signed displacement

Function:

If SF is equal to OF, then IP = IP + displacement (sign-extended to 16 bits).

Flags Affected:

None.

Description:

JGE and JNL transfer control to the target operand (IP + displacement) if the condition (SF xor OF = 0) is greater than or equal/not less than the tested value. These two mnemonics will generate the same instruction for the 8086/8088.

Example:

JGE label
JNL label

Encoding:

01111101	disp

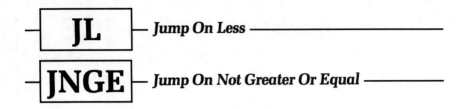

Mnemonic:

> JL   8-bit signed displacement
> JNGE 8-bit signed displacement

Function:

> If SF is not equal to OF, then IP = IP + displacement (sign-extended to 16 bits).

Flags Affected:

> None

Description:

> JL and JNGE transfer control to the target operand (IP + displacement) if the condition (SF xor OF = 1) is less than/not greater than or equal to the tested value. Both of these mnemonics will generate the same instruction for the 8086/8088.

Example:

> JL   label
> JNGE label

Encoding:

01111100	disp

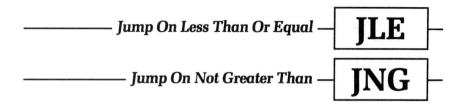

——————— *Jump On Less Than Or Equal* — **JLE** —

——————— *Jump On Not Greater Than* — **JNG** —

Mnemonic:

> JLE 8-bit signed label
> JNG 8-bit signed label

Function:

> If SF is not equal to OF or ZF = 1, then IP = IP + displacement
> (sign-extended to 16 bits).

Flags Affected:

> None

Description:

> JLE and JNG transfer control to the target operand (IP + dis-
> placement) if the condition SF xor OF = 1 or ZF = 1 is less than or
> equal to/not greater than the tested value. Both of these mnemon-
> ics will generate the same instruction for the 8086/8088.

Example:

> JLE label
> JNG label

Encoding:

01111110	disp

All mnemonics copyright Intel Corporation, 1981.

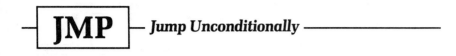

JMP — *Jump Unconditionally*

Mnemonic:

JMP target

Function:

If intra-segment, then IP = IP + signed displacement;
If inter-segment, then CS and IP are replaced by new values obtained from the instruction.

Flags Affected:

None

Description:

JMP unconditionally transfers control to the target location. The target operand may be obtained from the instruction itself (direct JMP), or from memory, or a register referenced by the instruction (indirect JMP).

An intra-segment direct JMP changes the instruction pointer by adding the relative displacement of the target from the JMP instruction. If the assembler can determine that the target is within 127 bytes of the JMP, it automatically generates a two-byte SHORT JMP instruction. Otherwise, the assembler will address a target within ± 32K.

An intra-segment JMP can be made by using memory or a 16-bit general register. In the first case, the word content referenced by the instruction replaces the IP. In the second case, the new IP value is taken from the register named in the instruction.

An inter-segment JMP replaces IP and CS with values contained in the instruction. The indirect inter-segment JMP may be made only through memory, with the first word of the double-word pointer referenced by the instruction replacing IP, and the second word replacing CS.

Example:

    JMP label
    JMP label.seg

Encoding:

Intra-Segment Direct

11101001	disp-low	disp-high

Intra-Segment Direct Short

Displacement is sign-extended to 16 bits

11101011	disp

Intra-Segment Indirect

11111111	mod 100 r/m

Inter-Segment Direct

11101010	offset-low	offset-high	seg-low	seg-high

Inter-Segment Indirect

11111111	mod 101 r/m

JNC — *Jump On Not Carry*

Mnemonic:

JNC 8-bit signed label

Function:

If CF = 0, then IP = IP + displacement (sign-extended to 16 bits).

Flags Affected:

None

Description:

JNC transfers control to the target operand (IP + displacement) on the condition CF = 0.

Example:

JNC label

Encoding:

01110011	disp

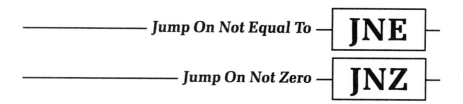

Jump On Not Equal To — **JNE**

Jump On Not Zero — **JNZ**

Mnemonic:

JNE 8-bit signed label

JNZ 8-bit signed label

Function:

If ZF = 0, then IP = IP + displacement (sign-extended to 16 bits).

Flags Affected:

None

Description:

JNE and JNZ transfer control to the target operand (IP + displacement) if the condition tested (ZF = 0) is true.

Example:

JNE label

JNZ label

Encoding:

01110101	disp

JNO — *Jump On Not Overflow*

Mnemonic:

JNO 8-bit signed displacement

Function:

If OF = 0, then IP = IP + displacement (sign-extended to 16 bits).

Flags Affected:

None

Description:

JNO transfers control to the target operand (IP + displacement) if the condition tested (OF = 0) is true.

Example:

JNO label

Encoding:

01110001	disp

Jump On Not Sign — JNS

Mnemonic:

JNS 8-bit displacement

Function:

If SF = 0, then IP = IP + displacement (sign-extended to 16 bits).

Flags Affected:

None

Description:

JNS transfers control to the target operand (IP + displacement) if the condition tested (SF = 0) is true.

Example:

JNS label

Encoding:

01111001	disp

Mnemonic:

JNP 8-bit signed displacement
JNO 8-bit signed displacement

Function:

If PF = 0, then IP = IP + displacement (sign-extended to 16 bits).

Flags Affected:

None

Description:

JNP and JPO transfer control to the target operand (IP + displacement) if the condition tested (PF = 0) is true. Both of these mnemonics will generate the same instruction for the 8086/8088.

Example:

JNP label
JPO label

Encoding:

01111011	disp

Jump On Overflow — | **JO** |

Mnemonic:

JO 8-bit signed displacement

Function:

If OF = 1, then IP = IP + displacement (sign-extended to 16 bits).

Flags Affected:

None

Description:

JO transfers control to the target operand (IP + displacement) if the tested condition (OF = 1) is true.

Example:

JO label

Encoding:

01110000	disp

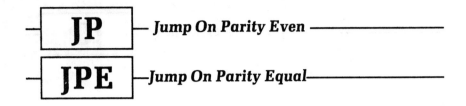

JP — Jump On Parity Even ——————

JPE —Jump On Parity Equal———————

Mnemonic:

> JP 8-bit signed displacement
> JPE 8-bit signed displacement

Function:

> If PF = 1, then IP = IP + displacement (sign-extended to 16 bits).

Flags Affected:

> None

Description:

> JP and JPE transfer control to the target operand (IP + displacement) if the condition tested (PF =) 1 is true.

Example:

> JP   label
> JPE label

Encoding:

01111010	disp

Jump On Sign— **JS**

Mnemonic:

JS 8-bit signed displacement

Function:

If SF = 1, then IP = IP + displacement (sign-extended to 16 bits).

Flags Affected:

None

Description:

JS transfers control to the target operand (IP + displacement) if the tested condition (SF = 1) is true.

Example:

JS label

Encoding:

01111000	disp

LAHF — *Load Register AH From Flags*

Mnemonic:

LAHF no operands

Function:

AH = d7 d6 d5 d4 d3 d2 d1 d0
   SF ZF X AF X PF X CF where x = undefined

Flags Affected:

None

Description:

LAHF (load register AH from flags) copies SF, ZF, AF, PF, CF into bits 7, 6, 5, 4, 2, 0, respectively, of register AH. The contents of bits 5, 3, and 1 are undefined.

Encoding:

10011111

———————————— *Load Pointer Using DS* — $\boxed{\textbf{LDS}}$ —

Mnemonic:

LDS destination, source

Function:

REG = data from source operand
DS   = data from source operand + 2

Flags Affected:

None

Description:

LDS transfers a 32-bit pointer variable from the source operand, which must be a memory operand, to the destination operand and register DS. The offset word of the pointer is transferred to the destination operand, which may be any 16-bit general register. The segment word of the pointer is transferred to register DS.

Example:

LDS SI, label

Encoding:

11000101	mod reg r/m

LEA —Load Effective Address

Mnemonic:

LEA destination, source

Function:

REG = offset of source operand

Flags Affected:

None

Description:

LEA transfers the offset of the source operand (rather than its value) to the destination operand. The source operand must be a memory operand and the destination operand must be a 16-bit general register.

Example:

LEA CX, label

Encoding:

10001101	mod reg r/m

—————————————*Load Pointer Using ES*—| **LES** |—

Mnemonic:

> LES destination, source

Function:

> REG = data from source address
> ES   = data from source address + 2

Flags Affected:

> None

Description:

> LES transfers a 32-bit pointer variable from the source operand, which must be a memory operand, to the destination operand and register ES. The offset word of the pointer is transferred to the destination operand, which may be any 16-bit general register. The segment word of the pointer is transferred to register ES.

Example:

> LES DI,label
> Label   0215h
> Label + 2   0457h
>
> *Before:*   *After:*
> DI = 0158h   DI = 0215h
> ES = 1005h   ES = 0457h

Encoding:

11000100	mod reg r/m

LOCK —Lock The Bus

Mnemonic:

> LOCK   MOV AX, Label

Function:

> None

Flags Affected:

> None

Description:

> LOCK is a one-byte prefix that causes the 8088 (configured in the maximum mode) to assert its bus LOCK signal while the following instruction executes.

Encoding:

11110000

Load String (Byte Or Word)—

Mnemonic:

LODS source-string

Function:

If byte-string: AL = data at memory addressed by SI:
  If DF = 0, then SI = SI + 1
  If DF = 0, then SI = SI − 1

If word-string: AX = data at memory addressed by SI:
  If DF = 0, then SI = SI + 2
  If DF = 0, then SI = SI − 2

Flags Affected:

None

Description:

LODS transfers the byte- or word-string element addressed by SI to register AL or AX, and updates SI to point to the next element in the string. The assembler uses the source-string specified in the instruction to determine the type and accessibility of the data.

Encoding:

1010110w

LOOP —*Loop If CX Not Zero*

Mnemonic:

LOOP 8-bit signed displacement

Function:

CX = CX – 1: If CX is not equal to zero, then IP = IP + displacement (sign-extended to 16 bits). If CX = 0, then the next sequential instruction is executed.

Flags Affected:

None

Description:

LOOP decrements CX by 1 and transfers control to the target operand if CX is not 0; otherwise, the instruction following LOOP is executed.

Encoding:

11100010	disp

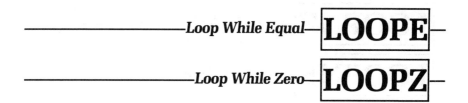

Loop While Equal—**LOOPE**—

Loop While Zero—**LOOPZ**—

Mnemonics:

>   LOOPE 8-bit signed displacement
>   LOOPZ 8-bit signed displacement

Function:

>   CX = CX − 1: If CX is not equal to zero and ZF = 1, then
>   IP = IP + displacement (sign-extended to 16 bits).

Flags Affected:

>   None

Description:

>   LOOPE and LOOPZ are different mnemonics for the same instruction. CX is decremented by 1, and control is transferred to the target operand if CX is not 0 and ZF = 1; otherwise, the instruction following LOOPE/LOOPZ is executed.

Example:

>   LOOPE label
>   LOOPZ label

Encoding:

11100001	disp

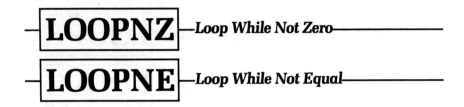

LOOPNZ —Loop While Not Zero

LOOPNE —Loop While Not Equal

Mnemonics:

LOOPNZ 8-bit signed displacement

Function:

CX = CX – 1: If CX is not equal to zero and ZF = 0, then
IP = IP + displacement (sign-extended to 16 bits).

Flags Affected:

None

Description:

LOOPNZ and LOOPNE are different mnemonics for the same
instruction. CX is decremented by 1, and control is transferred to
the target operand if CX is not 0 and ZF = 0; otherwise, the
instruction following LOOPNE/LOOPNZ is executed.

Example:

LOOPNZ label
LOOPNE label

Encoding:

11100000	disp

Move Byte Or Word **MOV**

Mnemonic:

MOV destination, source

Function:

Destination = source

Flags Affected:

None

Description:

MOV transfers a byte or word from the source operand to the
destination operand.

Example:

MOV AX,BX
MOV CL,AL
MOV BX,300
MOV BH,25

Encoding:

Memory or Register Operand to/from Register Operand:

100010dw	mod reg r/m

Immediate Operand to Memory or Register Operand:

1100011w	mod 000 r/m	data	data if w = 1

Immediate Operand to Register

1011wreg	data	data if w = 1

All mnemonics copyright Intel Corporation, 1981.

Memory Operand to Accumulator

1010000w	addr-low	addr-high

Accumulator to Memory Operand

1010001w	addr-low	addr-high

Memory or Register Operand to Segment Register

10001110	mod 0 reg r/m

Segment Register to Memory or Register Operand

10001100	mod 0 reg r/m

Move String —|MOVS|—

Mnemonic:

MOVS destination-string, source-string

Function:

Destination string = source string

Flags Affected:

None

Description:

MOVS transfers a byte or a word from the source string (addressed by SI) to the destination string (addressed by DI) and updates SI and DI to point to the next string element. When used with REP, MOVS performs a memory-to-memory block transfer. The source and destination string operands specified in the instruction are used by the assembler to determine type and accessability of the operands.

Example:

MOVS Buffer1, Buffer2

Encoding:

| 1010010w |

MUL — *Multiply*

Mnemonic:

MUL source

Function:

If byte source, then AX = AL × source (unsigned)
If word source, then AX, DX = AX × source (unsigned)

Flags Defined:

CF, OF

Flags Undefined:

AF, PF, SF, ZF

Description:

MUL performs an unsigned multiplication of the source operand and the accumulator. If the source is a byte, then it is multiplied by register AL, and the double-length result is returned in AH and AL. If the source operand is a word, then it is multiplied by register AX, and the double-length result is returned in registers DX and AX. The operands are treated as unsigned binary numbers. If the upper half of the result (AH for byte source, DX for word source) is non-zero, CF and OF are set; otherwise, they are cleared. When CF and OF are set, they indicate that AH or DX contains significant digits of the result.

Example:

MUL 25
MUL CX
MUL BL

Encoding:

1111011w	mod 100 r/m

Negate (form two's complement) **NEG**

Mnemonic:

NEG destination

Function:

Destination = 0 − Destination

Flags Defined:

AF, CF, OF, PF, SF, ZF

Description:

NEG subtracts the destination operand, which may be a byte or a word, from 0 and returns the result to the destination. This forms the two's complement of the number.

Encoding:

1111011w	mod 011 r/m

NOP —*No Operation*

Mnemonic:

>   NOP

Function:

>   None

Flags Affected:

>   None

Description:

>   NOP causes the CPU to do nothing.

Encoding:

> | 10010000 |

Logical Not— NOT

Mnemonic:

NOT destination

Function:

Destination = one's complement of destination

Flags Affected:

None

Description:

NOT inverts the bits (forms the one's complement) of the byte or word operand.

Example:

NOT AL

Encoding:

1111011w	mod 010 r/m

OR —Logical Or—

Mnemonic:

OR destination, source

Function:

Destination = Destination OR Source: CF = 0: OF = 0

Flags Defined:

CF, OF, PF, SF, ZF

Flags Undefined:

AF

Description:

OR performs the logical "inclusive or" of the two operands (byte or word) and returns the result to the destination operand. A bit in the result is set if either or both of the corresponding bits in the original operands is set; otherwise, the result bit is cleared.

Example:

OR AL,BL
OR AL,00111010B

Encoding:

Memory or Register Operand with Register Operand

000010dw	mod reg r/m

Immediate Operand to Memory or Register Operand

1000000w	mod 001 r/m	data	data if w = 1

Immediate Operand to Accumulator

0000110w	data	data if w = 1

OUT —Output

Mnemonic:

OUT port, accumulator

Function:

If AL is specified, then AL data is written to the port number.
If AX is specified, then AX is written to the port number and port
number + 1.

Flags Affected:

None

Description:

OUT transfers a byte or a word from the AL or AX register to an
output port. The port number may be specified either with an
immediate byte constant, allowing access to ports 0–255, or with
a number previously placed in register DX, allowing variable
access to ports 0–65,535.

Example:

OUT 45,AX
OUT DX,AL

Encoding:

Fixed Port

1110011w	port

Variable Port: DX is address of port

1110111w	Immediate Operand to Accumulator

—*Pop Stack*— POP

Mnemonic:

POP destination

Function:

Destination = data on top of stack: SP = SP + 2

Flags Affected:

None

Description:

POP transfers the word at the current top of the stack (pointed to by SP) to the destination operand, and then increments SP by 2, pointing to the new top of the stack.

Example:

POP DX
POP DS   CS is illegal to specify in POP

Encoding:

Memory or Register Operand

10001111	mod 000 r/m

Register Operand

01011reg

Segment Register

000reg111

All mnemonics copyright Intel Corporation, 1981.

POPF —Pop Flags

Mnemonic:

POPF

Function:

Flag bits are set with data from the top of the stack: SP = SP + 2

Flags Affected:

All

Description:

POPF transfers specific bits from the word at the current top of the stack (pointed to by register SP) into the flags, thus replacing whatever values the flags previously contained. SP is then incremented by 2.

POPF may also be used to set the value of TF, as no specific instruction does this.

Encoding:

```
10011100
```

——————————— *Push Data on Top of Stack* — PUSH —

Mnemonic:

PUSH source

Function:

SP = SP – 2: Source is pushed onto the top of the stack.

Flags Affected:

None

Description:

PUSH decrements SP (the stack pointer) by 2 and then transfers a word from the source operand to the top of the stack now pointed to by SP.

Example:

PUSH SI
PUSH ES CS is legal to push

Encoding:

Memory or Register Operand

11111111	mod 110 r/m

Register Operand

01010reg

Segment Register

000reg110

PUSHF — *Push Flags*

Mnemonic:

PUSHF

Function:

SP = SP − 2: Flag register is pushed onto the top of the stack.

Flags Affected:

None

Description:

PUSHF decrements SP (the stack pointer) by 2 and then transfers all flags to the word at the top of the stack pointed to by SP. The flags are not affected.

Encoding:

10011101

———————————— *Rotate Through Carry Left* —| **RCL** |—

Mnemonic:

RCL destination, count

Function:

(temp) = count: If temp is not equal to zero, then:
(temcary) = CF; CF = high-order bit of destination;
destination = (destination × 2) + (temcary);
(temp) = temp − 1; repeat function until temp = 0.
If count = 1, then: If high-order bit of destination is not equal to
CF, then OF = 1; otherwise, OF = 0.
If count is not equal to 1, then OF is undefined.

Flags Defined:

CF, OF

Description:

RCL rotates the bits in the byte or word destination operand to
the left by the number of bits specified in the count operand. The
carry flag (CF) is treated as "part of" the destination operand; that
is, its value is rotated into the low-order bit of the destination, and
it is replaced by the high-order bit of the destination.

Example:

RCL AL,3

Before:	*After:*	
AL = 01011110, CF = 0	AL = 10111100, CF = 0	1 count
AL = 10111100, CF = 0	AL = 01111000, CF = 1	2 count
AL = 01111000, CF = 1	AL = 11110001, CF = 0	3 count

Encoding:

110100vw	mod 010 r/m

If v = 0, then count = 1

All mnemonics copyright Intel Corporation, 1981.

| **RCR** | *— Rotate Through Carry Right* ———— |

Mnemonic:

RCR destination, count

Function:

(temp) = count: If temp is not equal to zero, then:
  (temcary) = CF: CF = low-order bit of destination;
  destination = destination / 2;
  high-order bit of destination = (temcary): (temp) = (temp) − 1.
If count = 1, then: If high-order bit of destination is not equal to
  next high-order bit of destination, then OF = 1; otherwise,
  OF = 0.
If count is not equal to 1, then OF is undefined.

Flags Affected:

CF, OF

Description:

RCR rotates the bits in the byte or word destination operand to
the right by the number of bits specified in the count operand. The
carry flag (CF) is treated as "part of" the destination operand; that
is, its value is rotated into the high-order bit of the destination, and
it is replaced by the low-order bit of the destination.

Example:

RCR BL,2

Before:	*After:*
BL = 11000010, CF = 1	BL = 11100001, CF = 0 1 count
BL = 11100001, CF = 0	BL = 01110000, CF = 1 2 count

Encoding:

110100vw	mod 011 r/m

If v = 0, then count = 1

All mnemonics copyright Intel Corporation, 1981.

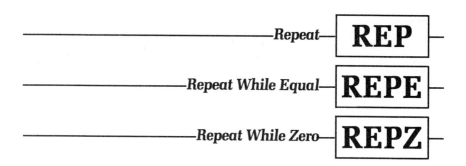

Repeat— **REP**

Repeat While Equal— **REPE**

Repeat While Zero— **REPZ**

Mnemonic:

REP MOVS destination, source

Flags Affected:

None

Description:

REP is used in conjunction with the MOVS (MOVE STRING) and STOS (STORE STRING) instructions and is interpreted as "repeat while not end-of-string" (CX not 0).

REPE and REPZ operate identically and are physically the same prefix byte as REP. These instructions are used with the CMPS (COMPARE STRING) and SCAS (SCAN STRING) instructions and require ZF (posted by these instructions) to be set before initiating the next repetition. ZF does not need to be initialized before executing the repeated string instruction.

Repeated string sequences are interruptible; the processor will recognize the interrupt before processing the next string element. System interrupt processing is not affected in any way. Upon return from the interrupt the repeated operation is resumed from the point of interruption.

Example:

```
REP  MOVS   destination, source
REPE CMPS   destination, source
```

Encoding:

1111001z

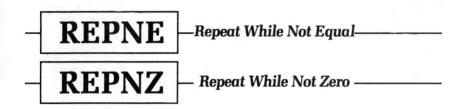

Mnemonic:

REPNE SCAS destination

Flags Affected:

None

Description:

REPNE and REPNZ operate identically and are physically the same prefix byte as REP. These instructions are used with the CMPS (COMPARE STRING) and SCAS (SCAN STRING) instructions. The ZF must be cleared or the repetition is terminated. ZF does not need to be initialized before executing the repeated string instruction.

Repeated string sequences are interruptible; the processor will recognize the interrupt before processing the next string element. System interrupt processing is not affected in any way. Upon return from the interrupt, the repeated operation is resumed from the point of interruption.

Example:

REPNE SCAS destination

Encoding:

```
1111001z
```

Return —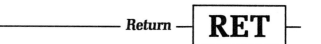

Mnemonic:

RET optional-pop-value

Function:

If intra-segment: IP is popped off the stack; SP = SP + 2
If inter-segment: CS is popped off the stack; SP = SP + 2
IP is popped off the stack; SP = SP + 2
If optional pop value is used, then SP = SP + value

Flags Affected:

None

Description:

RET transfers control from a procedure back to the instruction following the CALL that activated the procedure. The assembler generates an intra-segment RET if the programmer has defined the procedure NEAR, or an inter-segment RET if the procedure has been defined as FAR. RET pops the word at the top of the stack (pointed to by SP) into the instruction pointer and increments SP by 2. If RET is inter-segment, the word at the new top of the stack is popped onto the CS register, and SP is incremented by 2. If an optional pop value has been specified, RET adds that value to SP. This feature may be used to discard parameters pushed onto the stack, prior to the execution of the CALL instruction.

Example:

RET
RET 6

Encoding:

Intra-Segment

11000011

Intra-Segment and Add Immediate to Stack Pointer

11000010	data-low	data-high

Inter-Segment

11001011

Inter-Segment and Add Immediate to Stack Pointer

11001010	data-low	data-high

Rotate Left —  **ROL**

Mnemonic:

>ROL destination, count

Function:

>(temp) = count: If (temp) is not equal to zero, then:
>   CF = high-order bit of destination;
>   destination = destination × 2 + CF; (temp) = (temp) − 1.
>If count = 1, then: If high-order bit of destination is not equal to
>   CF, then OF = 1; otherwise, OF = 0:
>If count is not equal to 1, then OF is undefined.

Flags Defined:

>CF, OF

Description:

>ROL rotates the bits in the byte or word destination operand to
>the left by the number of bits specified in the count operand. If the
>count value equals 1, then it can be specified directly. If the count
>value is greater than 1, it must be set in the CL register prior to
>using this instruction.

Example:

>ROL BL,1
>MOV CL,2
>ROL BL,CL

Before:	After:	
BL = 11001100, CF = 0	BL = 10011001, CF = 1	1 count
BL = 10011001, CF = 1	BL = 00110011, CF = 1	2 count

Encoding:

110100vw	mod 000 r/m

If v = 0, then count = 1

All mnemonics copyright Intel Corporation, 1981.

ROR — Rotate Right

Mnemonic:

ROR destination, count

Function:

(temp) = count: If (temp) is not equal to zero then:
   CF = low-order bit of destination;
   destination = destination / 2;
   high-order bit of destination = CF;
   (temp) = (temp) − 1.
If count = 1, then: If high-order bit of destination is not equal to
   the next-to-high-order bit, then OF = 1; otherwise, OF = 0.
If count is not equal to 1, then OF is undefined.

Flags Affected:

CF, OF

Description:

ROR rotates the bits in the byte or word destination operand to
the right by the number of bits specified in the count operand. If
count equals 1, it may be specified directly. If count is greater than
1, it must be set in the CL register prior to using this instruction.

Example:

ROR BL,1
MOV CL,2
ROR, BL,CL

Before:	*After:*	
BL = 11001100, CF = 0	BL = 01100110, CF = 0	1 count
BL = 01100110, CF = 0	BL = 00110011, CF = 0	2 count

Encoding:

110100vw	mod 001 r/m

If v = 0, then count = 1

All mnemonics copyright Intel Corporation, 1981.

————————— *Store Registers AH into Flags* —| **SAHF** |—

Mnemonic:

SAHF

Function:

SF: ZF: X: AF: X: PF: X: CF:
d7 d6 d5 d4 d3 d2 d1 d0 AH transferred into flags

Flags Defined:

AF, CF, PF, SF, ZF

Description:

SAHF transfers bits 7, 6, 4, 2, and 0 from register AH into SF, ZF, AF, PF, and CF, respectively, thereby replacing whatever values these flags previously had. OF, DF, IF, and TF are not affected.

Encoding:

10011110

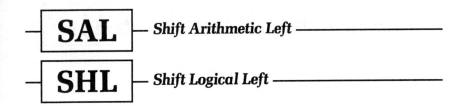

Mnemonic:

SAL destination, count
SHL destination, count

Function:

(temp) = count: If (temp) is not equal to zero, then:
   CF = high-order bit of destination;
   destination = destination × 2;
   low-order bit of destination = 0; (temp) = (temp) − 1.
If count = 1 then: If high-order bit of destination is not equal to the
   next-to-CF bit, then OF = 1; otherwise, OF = 0
If count is not equal to 1, then OF is undefined.

Flags Defined

CF, OF, PF, SF, ZF

Flags Undefined:

AF

Description:

SHL and SAL perform the same operation and are physically
the same instruction. The destination byte or word is shifted left
by the number of bits specified in the count operand. Zeroes are
shifted in on the right. If the sign bit retains its original value, then
OF is cleared. If count is equal to 1, it may be specified directly. If
count is greater than 1, its value must be loaded into the CL register prior to using this instruction.

Example:

SAL AL,1
MOV CL,2
SAL AL,CL

Before:	*After:*	
AL = 11001100, CF = 0	AL = 10011000, CF = 1	1 count
AL = 10011000, CF = 1	AL = 00110000, CF = 1	2 count

Encoding:

110100vw	mod 100 r/m

If v = 0, then count = 1

SAR —Shift Arithmetic Right

Mnemonic:

SAR destination, count

Function:

(temp) = count: If (temp) is not equal to zero, then:
CF = low-order bit of destination;
destination = destination / 2;
high-order bit of destination is the same as the previous high-order bit (sign bit); (temp) = temp) − 1
If count = 1, then: If high-order bit of destination is not equal to the next-to-next-to-high-order bit, then OF = 1;
otherwise, OF = 0.

Flags Defined:

CF, OF, PF, SF, ZF

Flags Undefined:

AF

Description:

SAR shifts the bits in the destination operand (byte or word) to the right by the number of bits specified in the count operand. Bits equal to the original high-order (sign) bit are shifted in on the left, thereby preserving the sign of the original value. Note that SAR does not produce the same result as the dividend of an "equivalent" IDIV instruction if the destination operand is negative and 1-bits are shifted out.

For example, shifting − 5 right by one bit yields − 3, while integer division − 5/2 yields − 2. The difference in the instructions is that IDIV truncates all numbers towards 0, while SAR truncates positive numbers towards 0 and negative numbers toward negative infinity.

All mnemonics copyright Intel Corporation, 1981.

If count is equal to 1, it may be specified directly. If count is greater than 1, its value must be loaded into the CL register prior to using this instruction.

Example:

SAR BL,1
MOV CL,2
SAR BL,CL

Before:	*After:*	
BL = 11001100, CF = 0	BL = 11100110, CF = 0	1 count
BL = 11100110, CF = 0	BL = 11110011, CF = 0	2 count

Encoding:

110100vw	mod 111 r/m

If $v = 0$, then count = 1

| **SBB** | — *Subtract with Borrow* ─────────

Mnemonic:

SBB destination, source

Function:

If CF = 1, then destination = destination – source – 1
If CF is not equal to 1, then destination = destination – source

Flags Defined:

AF, CF, OF, PF, SF, ZF

Description:

SBB subtracts the source from the destination, then subtracts 1 if CF is set, and returns the result to the destination operand. Both operands may be bytes or words. Both operands may be signed or unsigned binary numbers.

Encoding:

Memory or Register Operand and Register Operand

000110dw	mod reg r/m

Immediate Operand from Memory or Register Operand

100000sw	mod 011 r/m	data	data if s:w = 01

Immediate Operand from Accumulator

0001110w data	data if w = 1

Scan (byte or word) String— $\boxed{\textbf{SCAS}}$

Mnemonic:

SCAS destination-string

Function:

If byte destination-string, then the data addressed by the DI register is subtracted from AL. If DF = 0, then DI = DI + 1; if DF
= 1, then DI = DI − 1.

If word destination-string, then the data addressed by the DI register is subtracted from AX. If DF = 0, then DI = DI + 2; if DF
= 1, then DI = DI + 2.

Flags Defined:

AF, CF, OF, PF, SF, ZF

Description:

SCAS subtracts the destination string element (byte or word)
addressed by DI from the content of AL (byte string) or AX (word
string) and updates the flags, but does not alter the destination
string or the accumulator. SCAS also updates DI to point to the
next string element and AF, CF, OF, PF, SF and ZF to reflect the
relationship of the scanned value in AL/AX to the string element.
SCAS may be prefixed with REPE, REPZ, REPNE, or REPNZ.

Encoding:

1010111w

SHR — *Shift Logical Right*

Mnemonic:

SHR destination, source

Function:

(temp) = count; If (temp) is not equal to zero, then: CF = low-order bit of destination; destination = destination / 2; high-order bit of destination = 0; (temp) = (temp) − 1.

If count = 1, then: If high-order bit of destination is not equal to the next-to-next-to-high-order bit, then OF = 1; otherwise, OF = 0.

If count is not equal to 1, then OF is undefined.

Flags Defined:

CF, OF, PF, SF, ZF

Flags Undefined:

AF

Description:

SHR shifts the bits in the destination operand (byte or word) to the right by the number of bits specified by the count operand. Zeroes are shifted in on the left. If the sign bit retains the original value, then OF is cleared.

If count is equal to 1, it may be specified directly. If count is greater than 1, its value must be loaded into the CL register prior to execution of this instruction.

Example:

SHR BL,1
MOV CL,2
SHR BL,CL

All mnemonics copyright Intel Corporation, 1981.

Before: *After:*
BL = 00110011, CF = 0   BL = 00011001, CF = 1 1 count
BL = 00011001, CF = 1   BL = 00001100, CF = 1 2 count

Encoding:

110100vw	mod 101 r/m

If v = 0, then count = 1

STC — *Set Carry*

Mnemonic:

STC

Function:

CF = 1

Flag Defined:

CF

Description:

STC sets CF to 1 and affects no other flags.

Encoding:

11111001

Set Direction Flag— **STD**

Mnemonic:

STD

Function:

DF = 1

Flags Defined:

DF

Description:

STD sets DF to 1, causing the string instructions to auto-decrement the SI and/or DI index registers. STD does not affect any other flags. If DF is not set, the string instructions will auto-increment.

Encoding:

```
11111101
```

All mnemonics copyright Intel Corporation, 1981.

| **STI** | — *Set Interrupt-Enable Flag* ———————— |

Mnemonic:

STI

Function:

IF = 1

Flag Defined:

IF

Description:

STI sets IF to 1, thus enabling the CPU to recognize maskable interrupt requests appearing on the INTR input line. A pending interrupt will not actually be recognized until the instruction following STI has been executed. STI does not affect any other flags.

Encoding:

| 11111011 |

————————— *Store (byte or word) String* — $\boxed{\textbf{STOS}}$ —

Mnemonic:

STOS destination-string

Function:

If a byte, then the data in AL is stored in the address pointed to by DI.

If DF = 0, then DI = DI + 1. If DF = 1, then DI = DI − 1.

If a word, then the data in AX is stored in the address pointed to by DI.

If DF = 0, then DI = DI + 2. If DF = 1, then DI = DI − 2.

Flags Affected:

None

Description:

STOS transfers a byte or word from register AL or AX to the string element addressed by DI, and updates DI to point to the next location in the string.

Example:

STOS BYTE_DEST
STOS WORD_DEST
REP STOS BYTE_DEST1

Encoding:

1010101w

Mnemonic:

SUB destination, source

Function:

Destination = Destination − Source

Flags Defined:

AF, CF, OF, PF, SF, ZF

Description:

The source operand is subtracted from the destination operand, and the result replaces the destination operand. The operands may be bytes or words. Both operands may be signed or unsigned binary numbers.

Example:

SUB BX,AX
SUB BL,10
SUB SI,4790

Encoding:

Memory or Register Operand and Register Operand

001010dw	mod reg r/m

Immediate Operand from Memory or Register Operand

100000sw	mod 101 r/m	data	data if s:w = 01

Immediate Operand from Accumulator

0010110w	data	data if w = 1

Test (Logical Compare) — **TEST**

Mnemonic:

TEST destination, source

Function:

Destination is "anded" with Source. The flags are updated: CF = 0; OF = 0.

Flags Defined:

CF, OF, PF, SF, ZF

Flags Undefined:

AF

Description:

TEST performs the logical "and" of the two operands (byte or word), and updates the flags but does not return the result (i.e., neither operand is changed). If a test instruction is followed by a JNZ (jump if not zero) instruction, the jump will be taken if there are any corresponding 1-bits in both operands.

Example:

TEST AL,3FH
TEST BX,0557H

Encoding:

Memory or Register Operand with Register Operand

1000010w	mod reg r/m

All mnemonics copyright Intel Corporation, 1981.

Immediate Operand with Memory or Register Operand

1111011w	mod 000 r/m	data	data if w = 1

Immediate Operand with Accumulator

1010100w	data	data if w = 1

Wait— WAIT —

Mnemonic:

WAIT

Function:

None

Flags Affected:

None

Description:

WAIT causes the CPU to enter the wait state while its test line is not active.

Encoding:

10011011

XCHG —Exchange

Mnemonic:

XCHG destination, source

Function:

(Temp) = destination; destination = source; source = (Temp)

Flags Affected:

None

Description:

XCHG switches the contents of the source and destination (byte or word) operands.

Example:

XCHG BX,AX
XCHG label,CX

Encoding:

Memory or Register Operand with Register Operand

1000011w	mod reg r/m

Register Operand with Accumulator

10010reg

Translate—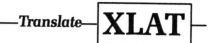

Mnemonic:

> XLAT Table__name

Function:

> AL = data at address pointed to by BX + AL

Flags Affected:

> None

Description:

> XLAT replaces a byte in the AL register with a byte from a 256-byte, user-coded translation table. Register BX is assumed to point to the beginning of the table. The byte in AL is used as an index into the table and is replaced by the byte at the offset in the table corresponding to AL's binary value. The first byte in the table has an offset of zero.
>
> For example, if AL contains 5H, and the sixth element of the translation table contains 33H, then AL will contain 33H after XLAT is executed.

Example:

> MOV BX, OFFSET__Table__Value
> XLAT Table__1

Encoding:

> | 11010111 |

 — *Exclusive or* ————————————————

Mnemonic:

XOR destination, source

Function:

Destination = Destination xor Source; CF = 0; OF = 0.

Flags Defined:

CF, OF, PF, SF, ZF

Flags Undefined:

AF

Description:

XOR performs the logical "exclusive or" of the two operands and returns the result to the destination operand. A bit in the result is set if the corresponding bits of the original operands contain opposite values.

Example:

XOR AX,BX

Before:	*After:*
AX = 5857H	AX = 00FFH
BX = 58A8H	BX = 58A8H

Encoding:

Memory or Register Operand with Register Operand

001100dw	mod reg r/m

Immediate Operand to Memory or Register Operand

1000000w	mod 110 r/m	data	data if w = 1

Immediate Operand to Accumulator

0011010w	data	data if w = 1

5
BASIC PROGRAMMING TECHNIQUES

INTRODUCTION

In this chapter we will examine some basic techniques for programming the 8086/8088. We will write simple arithmetic programs using many of the instructions discussed in Chapter 4. In addition, we will discuss subroutines and returns from subroutines. We will learn that due to the width of the 8086/8088 address bus, there are several different ways a subroutine can be called.

ARITHMETIC PROGRAMS

The arithmetic programs in this chapter will show you how to perform addition, subtraction, multiplication, and division with the 8086/8088. These programs will teach you how to perform integer arithmetic on positive binary numbers and on negative numbers represented as two's complement integers. We will start with an example of 8-bit addition. (Note, however, that the 8086/8088 is also capable of performing arithmetic operations with 16-bit numbers.)

8-BIT ADDITION

The addition program that follows is designed to add two 8-bit operands, OP1 and OP2, stored at memory addresses ADR1 and ADR2, respectively. The sum, stored at memory location ADR3, is called RES. Figure 5.1 shows a block diagram of how the operands and results are to be stored in memory.

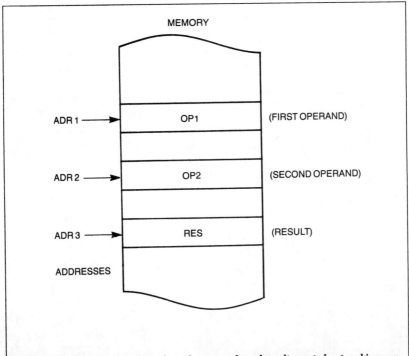

Figure 5.1: This diagram shows how the operands and results are to be stored in memory. OP1 is added to OP2 and stored in memory location RES.

Here is the program:

INSTRUCTION	COMMENT
MOV AL,ADR1	MOVE OP1 INTO AL
ADD AL,ADR2	ADD AL WITH OP2 @ ADR2
MOV ADR3,AL	SUM STORES @ ADR3

Each line of the program (expressed here in symbolic form) is called an *instruction*. Each instruction is translated by the computer into the corresponding object code on which the CPU can execute. Later in this discussion we will examine the object code for this program. Let's now take a look at the program.

The first line of the program specifies that the contents of the AL register (8-bit) be loaded with the data now in memory location ADR1. (*Note:* We could have specified any of the general 8-bit registers in the 8086/8088 CPU in place of the AL register.)

ADR1 is a symbolic representation of the actual address in the system memory. This address is defined elsewhere in the program. When the CPU reads the data from memory, the 16-bit value of ADR1 is then summed with the corresponding segment register to generate the 20-bit system address.

Referring back to the program, let's now examine the COMMENT field, the right-most field of each instruction line. Comments are very useful to the programmer for understanding and remembering exactly what each line of the program does. Comment fields are ignored when the object code is generated. Figure 5.2 shows the results after the first instruction is executed.

The second instruction:

ADD AL,ADR2

specifies that the data in memory address ADR2 be added to the contents of the 8-bit data in register AL. Address ADR2 contains the second operand, OP2. When the second instruction is executed, OP2 is read from memory and added to OP1. The result is stored in the AL register.

The sum of OP1 and OP2 is now contained in the AL register. To complete the program, we must transfer the contents of AL into the memory location ADR3. This is accomplished by the third line of the program:

MOV ADR3,AL

Going over this simple program, we can see that there are some important points about the 8086/8088 operation that we should discuss. One such point is that data is stored in bytes of memory. Thus, in this example, when the result was written in the memory at ADR3, only the byte ADR3 was disturbed. This is true even with the 16-bit data bus of the 8086. The CPU will electrically write a single byte in the system memory because an 8-bit register (AL) is used in the instruction.

Another interesting point about the program is that it transfers data from memory into an internal register. The location from which data is read is called the *source operand*. This operand is not changed during the execution of the program. If we were to examine the memory locations ADR1 and ADR2 at the conclusion of the program, we would find that they contain the same data that was originally present at the start of the program.

Let's now go on to assign actual numerical values to the address locations ADR1, ADR2 and ADR3. We can do this using "pseudo-instructions." Pseudo-instructions are instructions not used by the microprocessor, but used instead by the computer program that generates the object code. The pseudo-instruction we will use here is the EQUATE instruction—written as EQU. The name is derived from its function. This instruction equates or sets equal the two arguments on either side of the pseudo-instruction EQU. A complete program for this 8-bit addition is shown in Figure 5.3. In this program ADR1 equals 300H, ADR2 equals 320H, and ADR3 equals 345H.

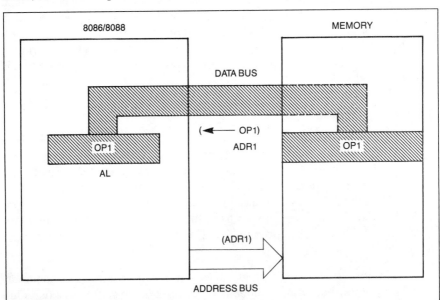

Figure 5.2: *After the MOV AL,OP1 instruction is executed, the lower 8 bits of the AX register will contain the value stored at memory location OP1.*

16-BIT ADDITION

Let us now extend this 8-bit addition problem to a 16-bit addition problem. A 16-bit problem can be solved in exactly the same way as an 8-bit problem except that there is a difference in the registers used and the number of memory locations taken up.

Recall that with the 8086 or 8088, a byte is a single memory location. Thus, a word (16 bits) will require two memory locations. Figure 5.4 shows

```
                    1 ;
                    2 ; PROGRAM TO ADD TWO 8-BIT NUMBERS
                    3 ;
                    4  ORG 0200H
                    5 ;
                    6 ADR1          EQU 0300H
                    7 ADR2          EQU 0320H
                    8 ADR3          EQU 0345H
                    9 ;
  0200 A00003      10 MOV AL,ADR1      ;LOAD AL WITH DATA @ ADR1
  0203 02062003    11 ADD AL,ADR2      ;ADD AL WITH DATA @ ADR2
  0207 A24503      12 MOV ADR3,AL      ;STORE AL @ ADR3
                   13 ;
```

Figure 5.3: This is an assembled 8086/8088 program for adding two 8-bit numbers.

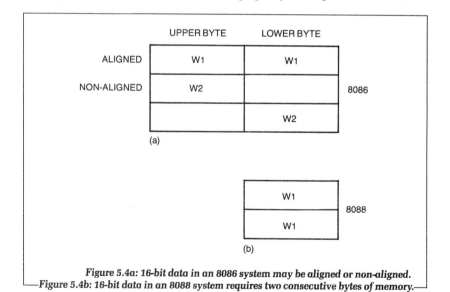

Figure 5.4a: 16-bit data in an 8086 system may be aligned or non-aligned.
Figure 5.4b: 16-bit data in an 8088 system requires two consecutive bytes of memory.

how the data is organized for 16-bit operations in the 8086/8088 system memory. A program for adding two 16-bit numbers is shown in Figure 5.5.

16-BIT SUBTRACTION

The subtraction of two 16-bit numbers with the 8086/8088 is similar to the 16-bit addition problem we solved earlier. Using the same example, we will now subtract OP2 from OP1 and store the results in ADR3. The data in memory will reside as shown in Figure 5.6. A program to perform the 16-bit subtraction is shown in Figure 5.7.

BCD ARITHMETIC

In Chapter 1 we discussed the concept of BCD arithmetic. Recall that BCD is used in applications in which it is imperative that every significant digit of the result be retained.

8-BIT BCD ADDITION

In BCD notation, a 4-bit nibble is used to store one decimal digit (0 – 9). As a result, every 8-bit byte can store two BCD digits. (This is called *packed BCD*.) Let us now see how BCD works. Let's add two bytes, each containing two BCD digits. A memory diagram of this example is shown in Figure 5.8.

```
                      1 ;
                      2 ; PROGRAM TO ADD TWO 16-BIT NUMBERS
                      3 ;
                      4  ORG 0250H
                      5 ;
                      6 ADR1        EQU 0300H
                      7 ADR2        EQU 0320H
                      8 ADR3        EQU 0345H
                      9 ;
      0250 A10003     10  MOV AX,ADR1    ;LOAD AX WITH DATA @ ADR1
      0253 03062003   11  ADD AX,ADR2    ;ADD AX WITH DATA @ ADR2
      0257 A34503     12  MOV ADR3,AX    ;STORE AX @ ADR3
                      13 ;
```

Figure 5.5: *This assembled 8086/8088 program for adding two 16-bit numbers is similar to the 8-bit program in Figure 5.3, with the exception that the AX register is used instead of the AL register.*

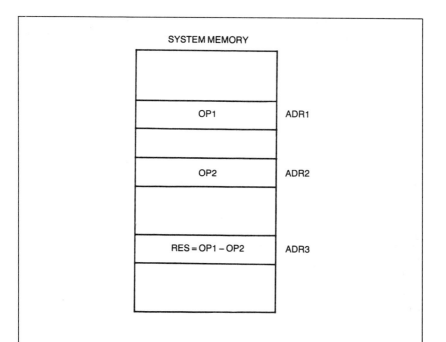

Figure 5.6: This memory diagram shows how the operands (OP1 and OP2) and the result will appear in a subtraction example.

```
                   1 ;
                   2 ; PROGRAM TO SUBTRACT TWO 16-BIT NUMBERS
                   3 ;
                   4  ORG 0250H
                   5 ;
                   6 ADR1        EQU 0300H
                   7 ADR2        EQU 0320H
                   8 ADR3        EQU 0345H
                   9 ;
0250 A10003       10  MOV AX,ADR1    ;LOAD AX WITH DATA @ ADR1
0253 2B062003     11  SUB AX,ADR2    ;ADD AX WITH DATA @ ADR2
0257 A34503       12  MOV ADR3,AX    ;STORE AX @ ADR3
                  13 ;
```

Figure 5.7: This is an assembled 8086/8088 program to perform a 16-bit subtraction.

Before we write any programs to perform BCD addition, let's first work with some numeric examples. This will help us define any problems that may arise from this type of addition. Let's first add 01 and 02.

01 is represented by: 00000001
02 is represented by: 00000010
The result is: 00000011

This result is the BCD representation for 03. (If you are not sure of the BCD equivalent, refer to the conversion table at the end of this book.) Everything worked quite simply in this case; so let's try another. Let's add **8** and 3.

08 is represented by: 00001000
03 is represented by: 00000011

If you have obtained 00001011 as your result, you have computed the binary sum of 8 and 3. This number is indeed 11 in binary. Unfortunately, 1011 is an illegal code in BCD. The BCD representation of 11 is 00010001.

This difference stems from the fact that the BCD representation uses only the first ten combinations of four digits to encode the decimal

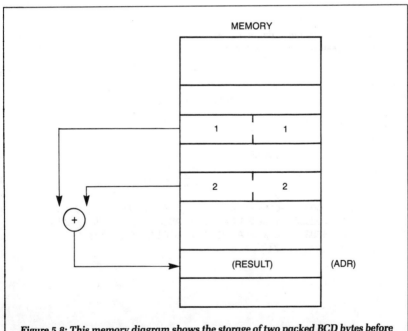

Figure 5.8: This memory diagram shows the storage of two packed BCD bytes before and after addition.

symbols 0 – 9. Thus, the remaining six possible combinations of four digits are unused in BCD notation. The number 1011 is one of these unused combinations. In other words, whenever the sum of two BCD digits is greater than 9, you must add 6 to the result in order to skip over the 6 unused codes.

The following example shows how to correct the previous example. By simply adding 6 to the binary equivalent of 11 (or the sum we just obtained by adding 8 and 3), we will obtain the correct result:

$$
\begin{array}{ll}
1011 & \textit{illegal BCD result} \\
\underline{0110} & + 6 \\
00010001 &
\end{array}
$$

This result is equal to 11 in BCD. We now have the correct answer to the BCD addition problem of 8 + 3.

This example illustrates one of the basic difficulties of the BCD mode: you must compensate for the six missing codes. There is, however, a special decimal addition adjust instruction (DAA) that will automatically adjust the result of the binary addition. (This instruction will add 6 if the result is greater than 9.)

We will now use this same example to illustrate another point about BCD arithmetic. When we add 6 to the result of 11, a carry is generated from the lower nibble into the upper nibble. This internal carry must be taken into account and added to the second BCD digit. Although the addition instruction automatically takes care of this problem, it is often convenient to be able to actually detect this internal carry from bit 3 to bit 4. This can be done by testing the AF flag. (Note: This carry is sometimes referred to as a half-carry or auxiliary carry.)

As an example, here are the program instructions for adding two BCD numbers, 11 and 22:

```
MOV AL,11H      11 INTO AL REGISTER
ADD AL,22H      ADD 11 TO 22 STORE IN AL
DAA             DECIMAL ADJUST THE RESULT
MOV ADR3,AL     STORE RESULT IN MEMORY
```

(Note: The H following the numbers 11 and 22 indicate these numbers are to be taken in hexadecimal notation, rather than decimal.) The AL register is used because the DAA instruction expects the operand to be in the AL register.

This program is similar to the one given for 8-bit binary addition. It does, however, use a new instruction: DAA (decimal adjust for addition). (Refer to Chapter 4 for more information on the DAA instruction.) Let's now see exactly what the DAA instruction does in this program.

The first event that occurs is that 11 and 22 are added. This will appear in the AL register like this:

```
  00010001  (11)
+ 00100010  (22)
= 00110011  (33)
```

Since the number in the lower 4 bits of the result is not greater than 9 and since there was no carry from bit 3 to bit 4, the DAA instruction did nothing to the lower 4 bits of the result. (AF equals 0.) Furthermore, there is no need to operate on the upper four bits of the result. Therefore, in this instance, the DAA instruction did not change the result in any way.

Let us take another example. We will add the numbers 22 and 39:

```
  00100010  (22)
+ 00111001  (39)
= 01011011  (5?)
```

1011 is an illegal BCD code, as it is greater than 9. The result must be corrected. We can use the DAA instruction, which will add 6 to the lower 4 bits and generate a carry into the next 4 bits. This will result in the following:

```
  01011011  (5?)
+ 00000110  (06)
= 01100001  (61)
```

This is the correct result for the addition of 22 and 39. In this case the DAA instruction was needed to generate the correct solution.

BCD SUBTRACTION

Performing BCD subtraction with the 8086/8088 is as simple as performing BCD addition. This is due to the fact that the CPU has a special DAS (decimal adjust for subtraction) instruction. (Refer to Chapter 4 for more information on this instruction.) Here is a program for subtracting two valid packed BCD numbers:

```
MOV AL,42H      LOAD AL WITH BCD 42
SUB AL,23H      SUBTRACT 23 FROM 42
DAS             DECIMAL ADJUST FOR SUBTRACTION
MOV ADR3,AL     STORE THE RESULT IN MEMORY
```

So far we have shown examples of addition and subtraction using different 8086/8088 instructions. Let's now examine the arithmetic operations
of multiplication and division.

MULTIPLICATION

Let's begin our study of multiplication by examining a simple decimal
multiplication problem. We will multiply 12 by 23:

$$
\begin{array}{r}
12 \\
\times\ 23 \\
\hline
36 \\
+\ 24 \\
\hline
276
\end{array}
$$

    12   *multiplicand*
  × 23   *multiplier*
    36   *partial product*
+ 24
  276   *final result*

The multiplication is performed by first multiplying the right-most digit
of the multiplier by the multiplicand, i.e., 3 × 12 (the partial product is 36),
and then multiplying the next digit of the multiplier (i.e., 2) by 12; then adding these two results to obtain the final result.

There is, however, one more operation: either 24 must be offset to the left
(or shifted left) by one digit position, or equivalently, the partial product (36)
must be shifted right by one position. The two numbers are then added.
The sum is 276.

Let us now examine binary multiplication. It is performed in the same
way as decimal multiplication. Let's multiply 5 × 3:

  (5)   101 *multiplicand*
  (3)   × 011 *multiplier*
          101 *partial product*
        101
     + 000
(15)   01111 *final result*

We can see from this example that binary multiplication is very similar to
decimal multiplication. We are fortunate in that the 8086/8088 is equipped
with an instruction that will perform this multiplication for us. Early
microprocessors, as well as 8-bit microprocessors, do not have a multiply
instruction. Therefore, multiplication is performed by a small program. In
fact, the only arithmetic these microprocessors can do is to add and shift.

Let us now examine how the multiply operation is performed on the
8086/8088.

MULTIPLYING 16-BIT NUMBERS

With the 8086/8088, it is possible to perform multiplication directly on two 16-bit numbers. When the operation is complete, the result is placed in two 16-bit registers. This is necessary because $2^{16} \times 2^{16}$ is equal to 2^{32}. Therefore, a 32-bit register is needed to hold the maximum possible answer obtained by multiplying two 16-bit numbers.

With the 8086/8088, one of the numbers to multiply is stored in the AX register. The double length (32-bit) result is stored in the DX and AX registers, with the most-significant 16-bits in the DX register.

If the multiply is to be an 8-bit operation, one of the numbers must be in the AL register. The 16-bit result is returned in the AX register, with the most-significant byte in AH.

Figure 5.9 presents a program for multiplying two 16-bit numbers and storing them in memory locations ADR3 and ADR4.

BINARY DIVISION

Let's start our discussion of binary division by examining decimal division. Let's divide 254 by 12:

$$
\begin{array}{r}
21 \ \ (quotient) \\
(divisor)\ 12\ \overline{\smash{)}254}\ \ (dividend) \\
-24 \\
\hline
14 \\
-12 \\
\hline
2\ \ (remainder)
\end{array}
$$

Examining this problem, we can see that the division is performed by subtracting the largest possible multiple of the divisor from the left-most digits of the dividend. (This generates a new dividend of 14.) The multiplier of the divisor now becomes the second digit of the quotient. Finally, the remainder is the result of the last possible subtraction.

To find the largest multiple of the divisor that can be subtracted from the dividend, we must make trial comparisons and subtractions. It should be noted that in determining the first digit of the quotient, the actual number is 20, not 2; and the number subtracted from the dividend is 240, not 24. By leaving the zeroes out, we are able to make notation convenient, but we must not lose sight of what is actually occurring in the process.

Binary division is performed in the same way, as can be seen in the following example:

$$
\begin{array}{r}
0011 \quad (quotient) \\
(divisor)\ 11\ \overline{)1010}\quad (dividend) \\
-\,11 \\
\hline
100 \\
-\,11 \\
\hline
1\quad (remainder)
\end{array}
$$

This example has followed the same procedure as the decimal example presented earlier. As we can see, the division results in a quotient and a remainder.

DIVISION WITH THE 8086/8088

The 8086/8088 provides a divide instruction that will perform a complete division operation for us. The dividend for the CPU is stored in the AX and DX registers. This means that the dividend is a 32-bit quantity, with the most-significant 16 bits being located in the DX register.

For this division, the divisor is a 16-bit quantity. When the operation is complete the 16-bit quotient is stored in the AX register. A 16-bit remainder is returned in the DX register.

When the division is performed on byte quantities, the 16-bit dividend is stored in the AX register. At the conclusion of the operation, the 8-bit

```
              1 ;
              2 ; 8086/8088 PROGRAM TO MULTIPLY
              3 ; TWO 16-BIT NUMBERS. THE NUMBERS WILL BE
              4 ; 2345 × 5378 = 12,611,410 = 00C06F52
              5 ;
              6  ORG 250H
              7 ;
              8 ADR3          EQU 300H
              9 ADR4          EQU ADR3 + 2
             10 ;
0250 B82909  11  MOV AX,#2345    ;2345 TO THE AX REGISTER
0253 B90215  12  MOV CX,#5378
0256 F7E1    13  MUL CX          ;MUL AX × (CX)5378
0258 A30003  14  MOV ADR3,AX     ;STORE AX IN ADR3 LOWER 16 BITS
025B 89160203 15  MOV ADR4,DX    ;STORE DX IN ADR4 UPPER 16 BITS
             16 ;
```

Figure 5.9: This is an assembled 8086/8088 program to multiply two 16-bit numbers.

quotient is returned to the AL register with the remainder being stored in the AH register.

Figure 5.10 shows an 8086/8088 program that will divide two numbers and store the quotient and remainder in memory.

SUBROUTINES

In this section we will examine how the 8086 and 8088 operate with subroutines. We will start by giving a general definition of a subroutine; we will then proceed with the details of using a subroutine with the CPU.

In concept, a *subroutine* is simply a block or section of instructions named by the programmer. A subroutine is executed when the main program executes the special CALL instruction; the subroutine is then terminated by a special instruction called a RETURN. Let us now illustrate the use of a subroutine in order to demonstrate its value.

Figure 5.11 illustrates how a subroutine is used. The main program appears on the left of the figure and the subroutine appears, symbolically, on the right. Let's examine how the subroutine works. In this program, the lines of the main program are executed successively until a CALL SUBROUTINE instruction is encountered. Execution of this instruction then results in a transfer to the subroutine section of the program. (Thus, the next instruction to be executed after the CALL SUBROUTINE is the first instruction in the subroutine.) This is illustrated by arrow 1 in Figure

```
               1 ;
               2 ; 8086/8088 PROGRAM TO DIVIDE TWO NUMBERS
               3 ; THE PROBLEM WILL BE TO DIVIDE 450 BY 20
               4 ; THIS WILL BE EQUAL TO 22 WITH A REMAINDER = 10
               5 ;
               6  ORG 250H
               7 ;
               8 ADR3    EQU 300H          ;2 BYTES FOR QUOTIENT
               9 ADR4    EQU ADR3 + 2      ;2 BYTES FOR REMAINDER
              10 ;
0250 31D2     11  XOR DX,DX          ;ZERO OUT DX REGISTER
0252 B8C201   12  MOV AX,#450        ;450 IS LOADED INTO AX
0255 B91600   13  MOV CX,#22         ;22 LOADED INTO CX
0258 F7F1     14  DIV CX             ;DIV DXAX BY CX (22)
025A A30003   15  MOV ADR3,AX        ;STORE QUOTIENT IN MEM
025D 89160203 16  MOV ADR4,DX        ;STORE REMAINDER IN MEM
              17 ;
```

Figure 5.10: This is an assembled 8086/8088 program to divide two 16-bit numbers.

5.11. (In this example, the section of the program that we are using as a subroutine executes like any other program, as indicated by arrow 2. In other words the subroutine does not contain any CALL SUBROUTINE instructions [described later].)

The last instruction of the subroutine is a RETURN. This special instruction causes the CPU to return to the main program. When the CPU returns to the main program, it will execute the instruction that comes immediately after the CALL SUBROUTINE instruction that initially forced the CPU to go to the subroutine section of the program. This is shown by arrow 3 in Figure 5.11.

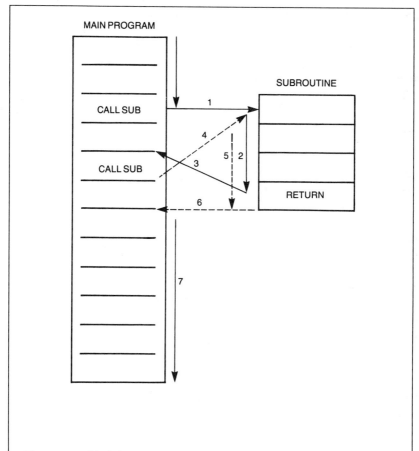

Figure 5.11: *A block diagram showing how a subroutine may be called from different locations in the main program. Solid arrows 1, 2, and 3 show the execution path for the first CALLSUB; the dotted arrows 4, 5, and 6 show the path for the second CALLSUB.*

Later, a second CALL SUBROUTINE instruction appears in the body of the main program. A new transfer occurs, as shown by arrow 4. This means that the body of the subroutine is again executed, following the CALL SUBROUTINE instruction.

Whenever a RETURN is encountered within a subroutine, a return occurs to the instruction that follows the CALL SUBROUTINE being executed. This is illustrated by arrow 6. Following the return to the main program, execution proceeds normally, as illustrated by arrow 7.

The effect of the two instructions, CALL SUBROUTINE and RETURN, should now be clear. What is the use of a subroutine? The essential value of a subroutine is that it can be called from any number of points in a main program, and the instructions in a subroutine can be used repeatedly without having to be rewritten. An advantage of this approach is that it saves memory space because the subroutine doesn't need to be rewritten each time. Another advantage is that the programmer needs to design a specific subroutine only once, as it can be used repeatedly. This is a significant simplification of the program design process.

IMPLEMENTATION OF THE SUBROUTINE MECHANISM

We will now discuss how the two instructions CALL SUBROUTINE and RETURN are implemented within the microprocessor. We will first discuss CALL SUBROUTINE. The CALL SUBROUTINE instruction causes a new address to be placed in the IP register of the CPU. Recall that the IP register determines the memory address from which the next instruction is executed. In other words, the start address of the subroutine is loaded into the IP register. But is that sufficient?

To answer this question, let us consider the other instruction: RETURN. This instruction causes a return to the main program instruction that follows the CALL SUBROUTINE. An action such as this can be possible only if the memory address of the instruction that follows the CALL SUBROUTINE is preserved somewhere.

The next problem is with saving this return address: it must always be saved in a location where it will not be erased.

When the CPU encounters a CALL SUBROUTINE instruction, the value of the IP register is saved automatically. At this time the IP register is equal to the address offset of the next instruction to be executed. In this case, it is the address of memory directly following the CALL SUBROUTINE instruction.

Next, the CPU starts execution at the address of the subroutine. When the RETURN instruction is executed in the subroutine, the saved value of the address is restored from the memory location where it was saved. Saving and restoring the address of the instruction after the CALL SUBROUTINE instruction is done automatically by the CPU. The CALL instruction saves the address, and the RETURN instruction restores the address.

We have previously stated that the address is saved in a specific location of memory. The question is, "Where in memory is the address saved?" It is saved in the location of memory designated as the stack. The stack is a special section of memory reserved for certain CPU operations. We will be showing these operations in later chapters of this text.

In Chapter 4 we presented the PUSH and POP instructions, which use the system stack. When a CALL SUBROUTINE instruction is encountered, the address of the next instruction to be executed is PUSHed onto the stack. That is where it is saved. When a RETURN instruction is encountered by the CPU, the saved address is automatically POPped off the stack. This popped address is then used as the address for the next instruction.

INTRA-SEGMENT CALL

There are two main types of subroutine CALLS: INTRA-SEGMENT and INTER-SEGMENT. Let's examine them.

The intra-segment CALL instruction causes the CPU to execute a subroutine that is located within the same 64K segment block of memory. When the 8086/8088 encounters this type of CALL, the IP register is pushed onto the stack. When a RETURN instruction is encountered, the IP register value is popped off the stack and placed again in the IP register of the CPU. See Figure 5.12.

INTER-SEGMENT CALL

This CALL causes the 8086/8088 to execute a subroutine that resides outside the 64K segment block of code. In this instance, both the CS (code segment) register and the IP register are pushed onto the stack. When a return instruction is encountered, both the CS and IP saved values are popped off and restored to the internal register of the CPU. This is shown in block diagram form in Figure 5.13.

CALL-RETURN MISMATCH

We can see from the preceding examples of intra-segment and inter-segment calls that the return instruction must either pop off the CS and IP

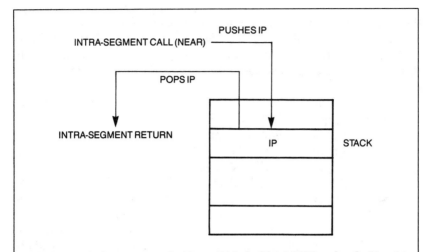

Figure 5.12: An intra-segment (inside a 64K block of data) CALL pushes the IP register on the system stack. The corresponding intra-segment RETURN pops the IP register off the stack.

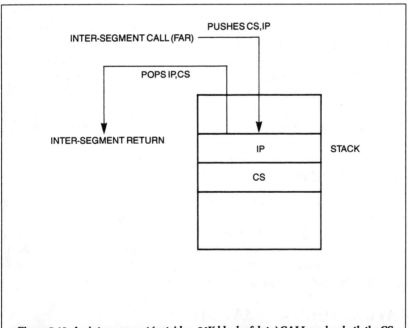

Figure 5.13: An inter-segment (outside a 64K block of data) CALL pushes both the CS and IP registers onto the system stack. An inter-segment RETURN pops both of these registers off the stack.

register, or pop off the IP register only. Due to this procedure, there must be more than one type of return instruction. There is. Recall from Chapter 4 that there are inter-segment and intra-segment RETURNs.

This means that a subroutine must always be used as either an intra-segment or an inter-segment routine. Figure 5.14 shows a CALL-RETURN mismatch.

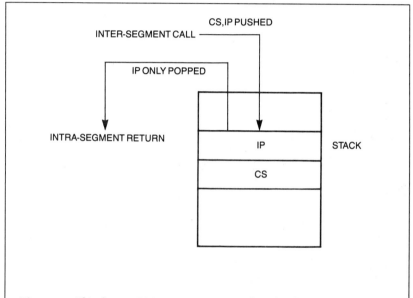

Figure 5.14: *This shows a CALL-RETURN mismatch. In this diagram an inter-segment CALL pushes both the CS and IP register on the stack. An intra-segment RETURN only pops off the IP register. This results in a CALL-RETURN mismatch and the program usually fails.*

SUMMARY

In this chapter we have presented some basic programming concepts. These have included binary addition, subtraction, multiplication, and division as well as BCD arithmetic. We have written several programs and explained how the 8086/8088 realizes these concepts.

Toward the end of this chapter we discussed the use of subroutines in programming. We examined how the 8086/8088 implements subroutine calls and returns, and we looked at both the inter-segment and intra-segment call and return. We will find this information useful when we discuss different programming applications involving the 8086/8088 in the chapters that follow.

6   INTERRUPTS FOR THE 8086/8088

INTRODUCTION

In this chapter we will discuss the general topic of interrupting the 8086 and 8088 microprocessors. We will first introduce the concept of an interrupt. We will then show how each different type of interrupt is handled electrically by the 8086 and 8088. In addition, we will examine useful examples of software, and we will discuss what actually occurs in the CPU during an interrupt operation.

WHAT IS AN INTERRUPT?

An example of an interrupt is best given through the following scenario. Picture this:

You are having a conversation with another person. A second person walks up and speaks your name—requesting your attention. The following is a list of possibilities for responding to this external request:

1. You can completely ignore the second person and continue your conversation with the first person.

2. You can get to a convenient stopping place in your conversation and then turn your attention to the second person.

3. You can *immediately* end your conversation with the first person, and start talking with the second person.

In any case, it is likely that when you have finished talking with the second person, you will want to continue your conversation with the first.

Although this scenario may seem simplistic, it accurately presents the concept of interrupts within a microprocessor system. Think of it this way. Think of yourself as being the 8086/8088 CPU. Think of the first person as being the main program being executed and the second person as being an external interrupt request (that is, as some hardware in the system that wishes the attention of the CPU). The 8086/8088 CPU must handle this request in some fashion. There are various ways this can be done. The three possibilities listed above are the most common.

With this general introduction to interrupts, let us now concentrate on the details of interrupts for the 8086/8088.

WHERE DO THE EXTERNAL INTERRUPT REQUESTS COME FROM?

A microprocessor system may be comprised of many different hardware components: a printer, a hard disk or floppy disk drive(s), a CRT, a timer, a control motor, or a digital to analog converter (a DAC)—just to name a few. Most of these external hardware components need the attention of the CPU only at certain times. At other times, they can function on their own.

For example, let's suppose your system has a clock as an external hardware device, which is designed to display the time of day on the CRT screen. In other words, as the screen is viewed, the clock hardware requires the CPU to read the time once each second and print it to the CRT screen. At all other times, the CPU is available to perform the other tasks required of it.

The main point here is that the external hardware of the clock does not need the attention of the CPU *all of the time*. The clock hardware electrically requests the CPU to read it, only when required. One way to accomplish this is through the CPU's interrupt system, whereby, once each second the CPU receives an external electrical interrupt request from the clock hardware. At this time, the CPU stops whatever it is doing and reads the clock time. After the clock has been read and the time displayed, the CPU will resume execution of the program it was running prior to the interrupt.

This simple example of an interrupt should help answer the initial question of where do the interrupt requests come from. The answer is that they come from the microprocessor system hardware.

NON-MASKABLE INTERRUPTS (NMI)

As shown in Figure 6.1, there are three main interrupt input lines on the 8086/8088 microprocessors: INTR, NMI and RESET. Each of these inputs can cause an external interrupt request to occur. In this section we will discuss the NMI or non-maskable interrupt input request. We will cover

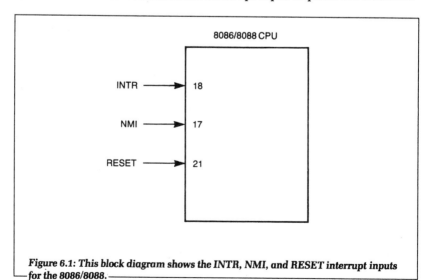

Figure 6.1: This block diagram shows the INTR, NMI, and RESET interrupt inputs for the 8086/8088.

several important points concerning 8086/8088 interrupts. Many of these points are common to other types of interrupt inputs as well. We shall begin our discussion with the non-maskable interrupt because it operates in only one way.

The term "non-maskable interrupt" means that this interrupt must always be recognized by the 8086/8088 as soon as electrically possible. (This was the third possibility in our previous list.) Since the 8086/8088 has a non-maskable interrupt, it follows that there must also be a maskable interrupt input. This is the INTR input. We will discuss this input later on in this chapter.

Let's assume that the NMI interrupt input has been externally asserted. The next question then is, "When will the NMI input be electrically recognized by the CPU?" Generally, it is recognized at the end of a current instruction cycle; that is, when the present instruction is complete. Note that there are some instructions on the 8086/8088 that can require quite a long time to execute (e.g., the divide and multiply instructions). The time required for the CPU to respond electrically to an interrupt request is known as *interrupt latency*. The actual amount of time depends on how many clock cycles are left in the current instruction.

CPU ACTIVITY DURING THE NMI REQUEST

During an NMI operation the first event to occur is that the FLAGS are pushed onto the system stack area. This action saves the current value of all the system flags. Next, the CPU clears the IF (the interrupt enable flag) and thus disables any interrupt from occurring on the INTR input line. When this flag is cleared, all interrupt requests from the INTR input are electrically ignored.

Next, a special flag on the 8086/8088, labeled TF (trap flag), is also cleared. This flag is used when the 8086/8088 is set into a single step mode. Therefore, clearing it determines that the 8086/8088 is no longer being used in the single step mode.

The next action taken by the CPU is to push the CS and the IP registers onto the system stack. At this point in the handling of the NMI by the CPU, the system stack appears as shown in Figure 6.2.

Finally, the CPU loads the IP register with the 16-bit value located at memory address 00008H. The CS register is then loaded with the 16-bit value located at address 0000AH. A new memory address is then generated, using the newly loaded CS and IP registers. Finally, the CPU starts execution of the code located at this new memory address.

In review, here are the steps taken when the CPU handles an NMI request:

1. The FLAG register is pushed onto the system stack.

2. The INTR inputs are disabled.

3. TF is cleared, no single step may occur.

4. The CS register is pushed onto the system stack.

5. The IP register is pushed onto the system stack.

6. The IP register is loaded with the 16-bit data at memory address 00008H.

7. The CS register is loaded with the 16-bit data at memory address 0000AH.

8. The CPU fetches the next instruction from the 20-bit address generated by the new CS and IP registers.

At this time, the CPU is executing the interrupt service routine for an NMI interrupt request.

THE INTERRUPT TABLE

Before proceeding with our discussion of the INTR input, let's examine the concept of the interrupt table. In our explanation of the NMI interrupt we stated that addresses 00008H and 0000AH are used for storage of the IP and CS registers. The values held in these registers are used to generate the new 20-bit address. These address values were obtained from a sequence

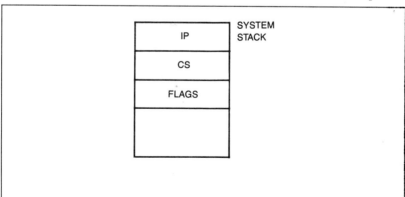

Figure 6.2: Here is how the system stack looks after the FLAGS, CS, and IP registers have been pushed onto the stack during the handling of an interrupt.

of addresses designated as the interrupt table. Figure 6.3 shows a diagram of the interrupt table for the 8086/8088. This interrupt table occupies the first 1024 bytes of system memory; that is, memory addresses 00000 – 003FF. There are 255 different types of interrupts that may be handled by the 8086/8088. Later on in this chapter we will discuss the topic of

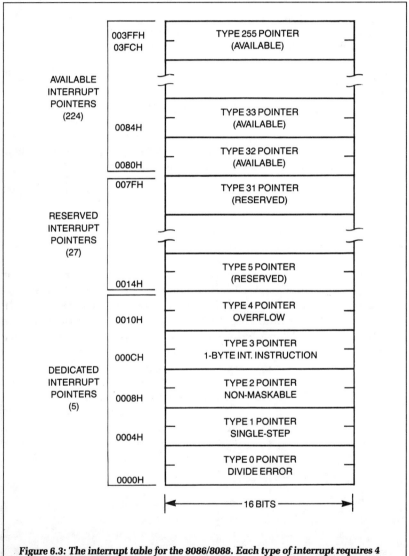

Figure 6.3: The interrupt table for the 8086/8088. Each type of interrupt requires 4 bytes of memory.

interrupt types in more detail. You will learn that each type is given a label, from type 0 – type 255.

For every type of interrupt (from 0 – 255) there are four memory bytes reserved in the interrupt table. These four bytes are required to store the 16-bit CS and IP registers used in generating the 20-bit address of the interrupt service routine. The first two bytes of the four bytes contain the value of the IP register. The last two bytes contain the value of the CS register, as shown in Figure 6.4.

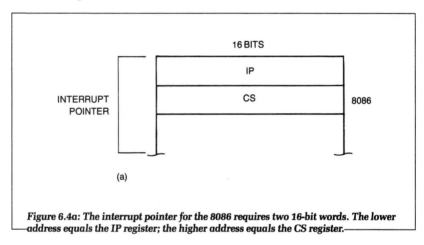

(a)

Figure 6.4a: The interrupt pointer for the 8086 requires two 16-bit words. The lower address equals the IP register; the higher address equals the CS register.

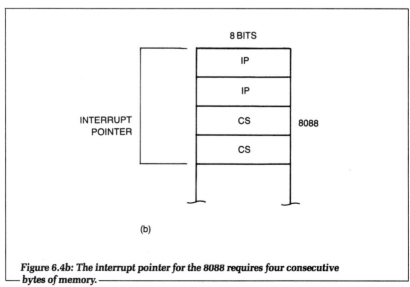

(b)

Figure 6.4b: The interrupt pointer for the 8088 requires four consecutive bytes of memory.

RESERVED INTERRUPT TYPES

Some of the 255 possible interrupt types are reserved for specific uses. The following is a list of type 0 – type 4 interrupts and their specific uses in the system:

Type 0	Reserved for division by 0
Type 1	Reserved for single stepping
Type 2	Reserved for NMI interrupts
Type 3	Reserved for 1-byte software interrupt instruction
Type 4	Reserved for signed overflow interrupt

(*Note:* The Intel Corporation [the designer of the 8086/8088] has requested that interrupt types 5 – 31 [memory addresses 00014H – 0007FH] be reserved for future Intel products. In other words, if you use an interrupt type 5 – 31, your system may not be able to use some future product designed by Intel.)

INTR INPUT

Let's now discuss the INTR input. This interrupt input can be logically enabled and disabled with software. When it is disabled, the CPU will not honor any external requests—in fact, it can be thought of as not even existing on the CPU. In Chapter 4 we discussed the CLI (clear interrupt) instruction. This software instruction is used to disable the INTR input.

We can enable the INTR input to the 8086/8088 CPU by using the STI (set interrupt flag) instruction. As an example, let's assume that the INTR input has been enabled and an external request has been asserted. The following discussion will explain how the CPU handles these types of requests.

When the INTR input has been honored by the CPU, an external signal, called *interrupt acknowledge*, is generated. This signal allows the hardware of the system to place an 8-bit value, called the *interrupt type*, on the system data bus. Recall that there are 255 different types.

The CPU next reads the interrupt type from the data bus and computes the address for the type in the interrupt table. This is done by multiplying by 4, the type number read from the system data bus. For example, let's suppose the external hardware places a 2FH on the system data bus when the interrupt acknowledge is asserted. 2F is the type number. The address for this type number in the interrupt table is 4 × 2FH, which is 000BCH.

Next, the flags are pushed onto the system stack. Following this the interrupts are disabled.

The CPU now pushes the IP and CS registers onto the system stack. After this, the CPU loads the new values for the CS and IP registers from memory locations 000BCH – 000BFH. When these registers are loaded, the microprocessor fetches the next instruction from the 20-bit address generated by the new CS and IP registers.

Let's now review the list of operations that the CPU performs when handling an INTR request:

1. An external interrupt acknowledge signal is generated.

2. A type code 0 – 255 is read from the system data bus.

3. The flag register is pushed onto the system stack.

4. The interrupts and single step mode are disabled.

5. The CS and IP registers are pushed onto the system stack.

6. The IP register is loaded from data at memory address (TYPE × 4) and (TYPE × 4) + 1.

7. The CS register is loaded from data at memory address (TYPE × 4) + 2 and (TYPE × 4) + 3.

8. The CPU fetches the next instruction from the 20-bit memory address generated by the new value of the CS and IP registers just loaded from the interrupt table.

Figure 6.5 shows a flowchart of the events that occur during the handling of interrupts with the 8086/8088.

INTERNAL INTERRUPTS

External interrupts are only one way of generating interrupt types with the 8086/8088. Another technique for generating interrupts is via software. Using special software instructions, it is possible to enable the CPU to respond to any interrupt type, 0 – 255. Here is how it is done.

One software instruction that generates an interrupt is INT (presented in Chapter 4). There are two ways of using this particular instruction—as either a 1-byte or a 2-byte instruction. If you use a 1-byte INT instruction, it is encoded as CCH.

When the CPU executes this 1-byte instruction, a type-3 interrupt is automatically generated in exactly the same manner as the INTR input.

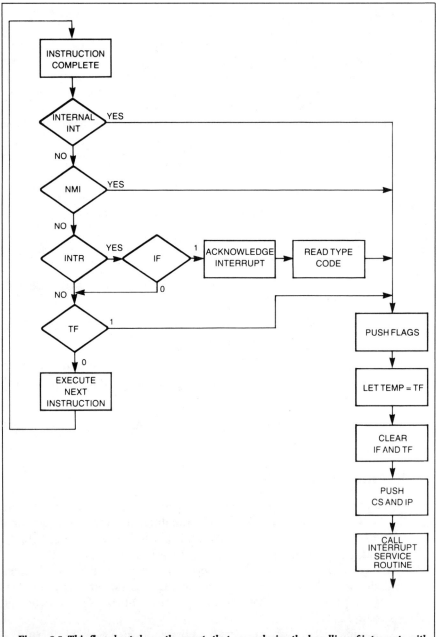

Figure 6.5: This flowchart shows the events that occur during the handling of interrupts with the 8086/8088.

However, unlike the INTR input to the microprocessor, the software interrupt cannot be disabled or masked.

Let us now assume that we are using the 2-byte version of the INT instruction. The first byte would be encoded as CDH. The second byte would be equal to an 8-bit number between 0 – 255 (inclusive). This number defines the interrupt TYPE you wish to generate.

For example, let's suppose you wish to generate an interrupt type 96H. The 2-byte INT instruction would be encoded as CD96H. The interrupt table address in hexadecimal for the IP would be equal to 4 × 96H = 258 in hexadecimal. Addresses 258H and 259H would contain the IP register value for the interrupt service routine. Addresses 25AH and 25BH would contain the CS register value for the interrupt service routine.

INTERRUPT ON OVERFLOW

There is another software instruction that can cause an automatic generation of a type 4 interrupt: the INTO instruction. When the overflow flag (OF) is set, and this instruction is executed, an internal interrupt is generated. Refer to chapter 1 for a complete discussion of what an overflow means.

RETURN FROM INTERRUPT

Now that we have learned how the CPU starts execution of an interrupt service routine, let us discuss how the CPU gets back to the main program from the service routine. When the CPU first enters the service routine, the FLAGS, CS, and IP registers are saved. This is essentially the information needed to return the CPU to the address it held prior to the interrupt.

During the execution of the interrupt service routine, you can change the values of some internal registers. If it is important that you save the original value of these registers, it is wise to PUSH them onto the stack. Figure 6.6 shows a typical start of an interrupt service routine.

Another point to note about entering an interrupt service routine is that all the interrupts have been disabled. If you wish other interrupts to be honored by the CPU while servicing this interrupt, the set interrupt flag (STI) instruction should be one of the first instructions you execute in the interrupt service routine. This is demonstrated by the partial program in Figure 6.7.

Let's assume we have completed the servicing of the interrupt. How do we return to the main program? We use the RETI instruction. When this instruction is executed the FLAGs, IP, and CS registers are popped off the stack. Before returning to the main program it is important to insure that the interrupts are again enabled (if this is desired). Further it is necessary to pop off any internal registers that were pushed onto the system stack during the interrupt service routine. Figure 6.8 shows a sample interrupt service routine that demonstrates all of these points.

RESETTING THE 8086/8088

In the preceding examples we have shown how the NMI, INTR, and SOFTWARE interrupts operate for the CPU. Let us now discuss another type of interrupt: the RESET input on the 8086/8088. When the reset input

```
;
;   START OF INTERRUPT SERVICE ROUTINE
;
        PUSH AX          ;SAVE AX REG
        PUSH BX          ;SAVE BX REG
        PUSH CX          ;SAVE CX REG
        PUSH DX          ;SAVE DX REG
;
;   NOW START THE ACTUAL CODE FOR THE INTERRUPT ROUTINE
;
        MOV AX,NUM
```

Figure 6.6: *A typical start of an interrupt service routine that shows how important registers are saved on the stack.*

```
;
;   START OF INTERRUPT SERVICE ROUTINE
;
        STI              ;TURN ON INTERRUPTS AGAIN
        PUSH AX          ;SAVE AX REG
        PUSH BX          ;SAVE BX REG
        PUSH CX          ;SAVE CX REG
        PUSH DX          ;SAVE DX REG
;
;   NOW START THE ACTUAL CODE FOR THE INTERRUPT ROUTINE
;
        MOV AX,NUM
```

Figure 6.7: *This diagram shows the start of an interrupt routine that allows further interrupts. This is made possible, early in the service routine, by the STI instruction.*

```
;
;   START OF INTERRUPT SERVICE ROUTINE
;
        PUSH AX          ;SAVE AX REG
        PUSH BX          ;SAVE BX REG
        PUSH CX          ;SAVE CX REG
        PUSH DX          ;SAVE DX REG
;
;   NOW START THE ACTUAL CODE FOR THE INTERRUPT ROUTINE
;
        MOV AX,NUM
        MUL AX,BX
;
;   MORE OF THE ROUTINE GOES HERE
;
;   END OF THE ROUTINE
;
        POP DX
        POP CX
        POP BX
        POP AX
        STI              ;TURN ON INTERRUPTS
        RETI             ;RETURN FROM INTERRUPTS
```

Figure 6.8: A sample interrupt routine for the 8086/8088.

line is asserted, the CPU starts execution in one, and only one, way. This allows for an orderly start, restart, or power-up of the system.

Following the assertion of the RESET input line, the CPU registers are initialized in the following way:

FLAGS = Clear

Instruction Pointer = 0000H

CS register = FFFFH

DS register = 0000H

SS register = 0000H

ES register = 0000H

Based on these register definitions, after reset, the first instruction will be fetched from the following location:

$(CS \times 16) + IP = FFFF0H + 0000H = FFFF0H$

The first location after reset is in high memory absolute location FFFF0H.

Recall that the manufacturer recommends that these high memory locations, FFFF0H to FFFFFH, not be used except for their intended purposes. The total reserved memory locations for the 8086/8088 are shown in Figure 6.9.

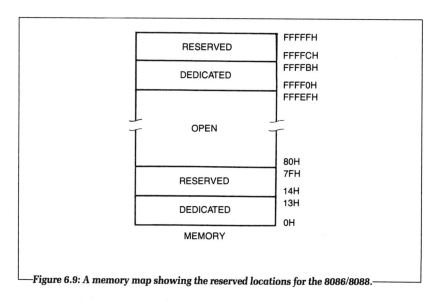

Figure 6.9: A memory map showing the reserved locations for the 8086/8088.

CHAPTER SUMMARY

In this chapter we have examined interrupts for the 8086/8088. Our discussion began with a general introduction of an interrupt. From there we proceeded to discuss both the maskable "INTR" and non-maskable "NMI" interrupts. In each case, we explained how the interrupt request is handled by the CPU.

Next, we discussed how the CPU generates internal interrupts using the INT and INTO instructions. We finished the chapter by showing how the 8086/8088 responds internally to a reset.

Once you understand the information in this chapter, you should be able to better understand how the CPU can be programmed to handle different interrupt requests from the peripheral system hardware.

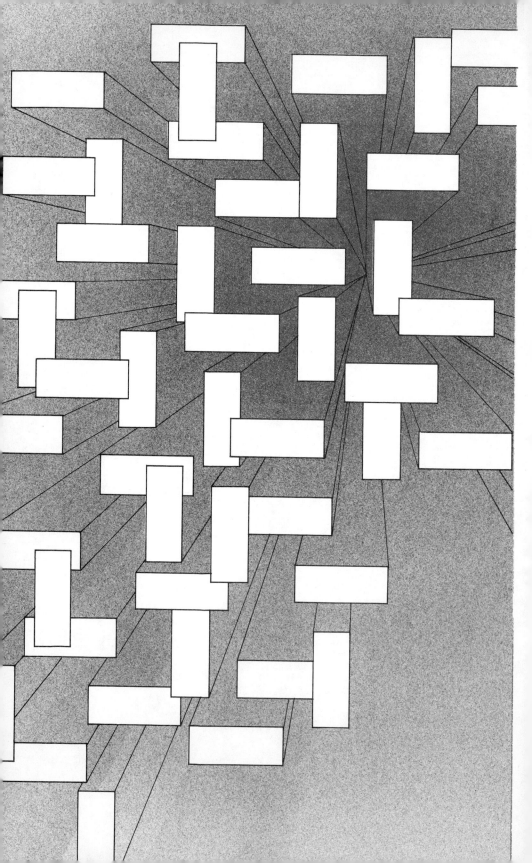

7 INPUT AND OUTPUT FOR THE 8086/8088

INTRODUCTION

An 8086/8088 system generally consists of one or more input and/or output devices. In this chapter we will discuss the input/output (I/O) architecture of the 8086/8088 CPU. We will also present the special instructions for I/O and an explanation of how they can be used. We will give several examples showing how an 8086/8088 interfaces with and controls different I/O devices.

WHAT IS INPUT AND OUTPUT?

In Chapter 2 we examined the general architecture of a microprocessor-based system. Figure 7.1 provides a quick review. In this figure we can see that the microprocessor communicates with ROM, RAM, and I/O. ROM and RAM are grouped together to make up the system memory (input/output). With the 8086/8088, the system memory has valid addresses from 00000H to FFFFFH. Note that the I/O block is not included in this memory space.

Some microprocessors allocate some of the available memory space for I/O. These microprocessors include the 6800, the 6502, the 6809, and the 68000—to name just a few. Microprocessors that use memory space for I/O are said to use "memory-mapped I/O."

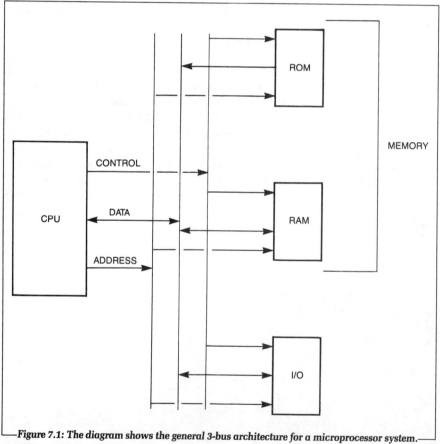

Figure 7.1: The diagram shows the general 3-bus architecture for a microprocessor system.

The 8086 and 8088 do not use memory-mapped I/O. Thus, all the system memory space can be used for memory, as the system I/O has its own address space. An I/O architecture like this is called "I/O-mapped I/O."

An I/O operation can be defined as follows:

> **Input:** When the microprocessor reads data from a source that is not system memory.

> **Output:** When the microprocessor writes data to a destination that is not system memory.

We stated earlier in this text that the system control bus defines the type of communication that occurs. In other words, if the system uses "I/O-mapped I/O," there are separate control lines for the I/O and memory systems. For example, the memory system uses control lines labeled memory read and memory write, while the I/O system uses control lines labeled input read and output write. See Figure 7.2.

I/O ADDRESSING

In a typical microprocessor system there are usually several I/O ports. (Note: A *port* is a unique place to read or write data that is not system memory. In fact, a port is similar to a unique location in the system memory from which data will be read or written to during a memory operation.) Each port in the I/O system is given a unique address, called the *port*

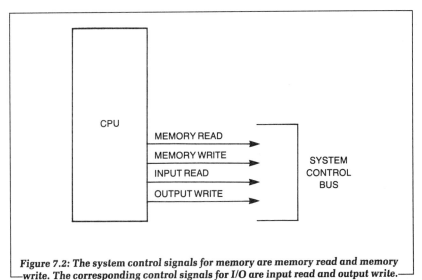

Figure 7.2: The system control signals for memory are memory read and memory write. The corresponding control signals for I/O are input read and output write.

select code. (See Figure 7.3.) To generate the port select code, the system address lines A0-A15 are decoded with logic to respond to a specific combination. For example, a port may have a port select code of 0057H, as shown in Figure 7.4.

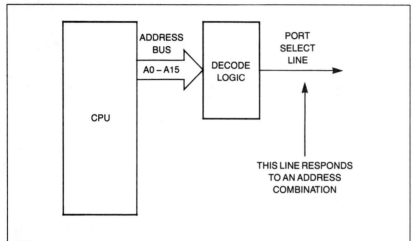

Figure 7.3: *Each I/O port in the system is designed to respond electrically to a unique combination on the system address bus.*

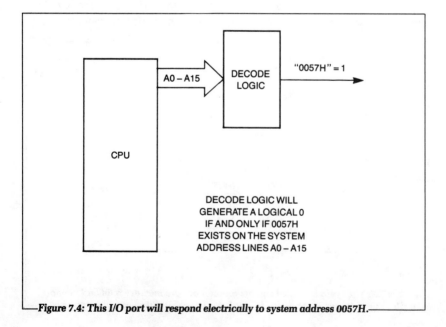

Figure 7.4: *This I/O port will respond electrically to system address 0057H.*

For the 8086/8088 there are only 16 address lines out of the 20 (total) microprocessor address lines available for I/O addressing. This gives a total of 65,535 input and output ports available in the system. Figure 7.5 shows a memory map of the space available for I/O with the 8086/8088.

Although the I/O system and the memory system are completely separate, these two systems use the same address lines. This means that you can have a memory address of 00F4H and an I/O address of 00F4H. A distinction can be made between these two systems by reviewing the lines in the system control bus: during a memory operation the memory read or memory write control line is active; and during an I/O operation the input read or output write line is active.

RESERVED I/O SPACE

Figure 7.5 shows an area of I/O space—addresses 00F8H–00FFH—which is labeled "reserved." This area is labeled "reserved" because Intel Corporation has requested that it not be used for your system application, as it is meant to be used for future Intel products.

WHAT IS AN I/O DEVICE?

An *I/O device* may be defined as any hardware that the system controls. Such a device may have one or more I/O ports or I/O addresses associated

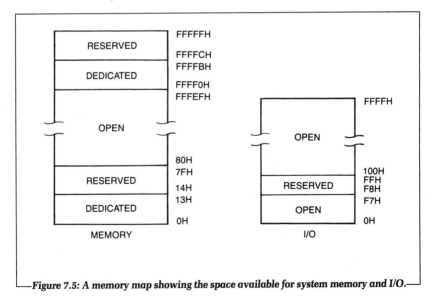

Figure 7.5: A memory map showing the space available for system memory and I/O.

with it, as shown in Figure 7.6. Examples of I/O devices are LSI (large scale integration) chips, such as a floppy disk controller or a timer chip.

INPUT INSTRUCTION

The IN instruction is used to read data from an input port on the microprocessor. This instruction is written as:

>   IN accumulator,port

The IN instruction transfers a byte or word of data to the accumulator from an input port address. If the transfer is a byte of data, it is stored in the AL register; if it is a word, it is placed in the AX register.

FIXED PORT ADDRESSING

There are two ways to use the IN instruction—with either fixed or variable port. When a *fixed port* IN instruction is used, it is encoded, as shown in Figure 7.7. We can see in this figure that the first byte has the W bit set to a either logical 1 or 0. If W is set to a logical 1, the transfer is a word (16 bits), and the data ends up in the AX register. If it is set to a logical 0, the transfer is a byte, and the data ends up in the AL register.

The second byte shown in Figure 7.7 is an 8-bit port address. Since there are only 8 bits, a total of 255 unique I/O ports can be accessed using this instruction. As an example of using this instruction, let's suppose that we

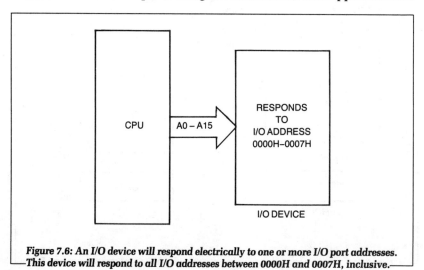

Figure 7.6: An I/O device will respond electrically to one or more I/O port addresses. This device will respond to all I/O addresses between 0000H and 0007H, inclusive.

are reading byte data at port 3DH. The instruction encoding should appear as shown in Figure 7.8. The way to specify a byte or word transfer is like this:

        IN AX,port (word)
        IN AL,port (byte)

VARIABLE PORT ADDRESSING

Another way the IN instruction may be used is with variable port. Using variable port encoding gives you access to all 16 bits of the system address bus for I/O addressing. The encoding of the variable port format for the IN instruction is shown in Figure 7.9.

Viewing Figure 7.9, we can see that only one byte is required to use this instruction. The W bit equals 1 if word data is wanted; it equals 0 if byte data is wanted. The address for the port is contained in the DX register at the time this instruction is executed. Using the DX register gives 16 bits of address that can be modified under program control. For example, we can use the variable port format of the IN instruction to read word data from port 05ACH. The program shown in Figure 7.10 will accomplish this.

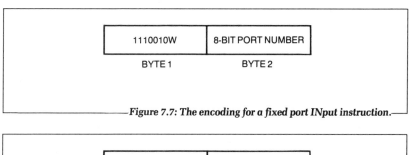

Figure 7.7: The encoding for a fixed port INput instruction.

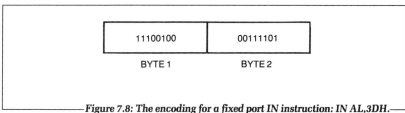

Figure 7.8: The encoding for a fixed port IN instruction: IN AL,3DH.

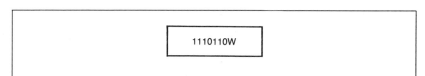

Figure 7.9: This shows the encoding for a variable port INput instruction. The address will be contained in the DX register of the CPU.

OUTPUT INSTRUCTION

The OUT instruction is used to transfer data from the CPU to an output port. This instruction has a similar format to the IN instruction. Its format is:

OUT port,accumulator

Like the INput instruction, the OUTput instruction can be used with either fixed or variable port format. Figure 7.11 shows examples of two small programs that use the OUT instruction in the fixed and variable port formats.

```
              1  ;
              2  ;  PROGRAM TO USE THE VARIABLE PORT
              3  ;  MODE FOR THE IN INSTRUCTION
              4  ;  16-BIT PORT NUMBER = 05AC
              5  ;
0000 BAAC05   6          MOV DX,#05ACH    ;PORT NUMBER TO THE DX REG
0003 ED       7          IN AX,DX                 ;INPUT WORD TO AX FROM DX
              8  ;
```

Figure 7.10: An 8086/8088 program showing the variable port IN instruction in use.

```
              1  ;
              2  ;
0000 BAAC05   3          MOV DX,#05ACH        ;LOAD ADDRESS INTO DX REG
0003 EC       4          IN AL,DX             ;INPUT BYTE TO AL FROM ADD IN DX
              5  ;
              6  ;  NOW TO OUTPUT BYTE USING VARIABLE PORT FORMAT
              7  ;
0004 BA8704   8          MOV DX,#0487H        ;LOAD ADDRESS INTO DX REG
0007 EE       9          OUT DX,AL    ;OUTPUT DATA TO VARIABLE PORT
             10  ;
             11  ;
0008 E607    12          OUT 07H,AL           ;OUTPUT BYTE TO FIXED PORT = 07
             13  ;
```

Figure 7.11: This 8086/8088 program shows how the fixed and variable port OUTput instruction is used.

8086 INPUT AND OUTPUT PORTS

When using the 8086, we should remember that it has a 16-bit data bus. This means that the addresses of the ports must be consistent with the data byte (i.e., either high or low). When a byte port has an even address, it must be physically connected to the lower byte (D0–D7) of the 16-bit data bus. An odd address byte port must be physically connected to the upper byte (F8-D15) of the system data bus. A word port address should be specified as an even address, as shown in Figure 7.12.

8088 INPUT AND OUTPUT PORTS

If you are using an 8088 CPU that has an 8-bit data bus, you can use both word and byte output ports. The same conventions that we discussed for the 8086 may be followed for the 8088. However, there is no need to be concerned about an even or odd addressed byte port, since there is only one way to connect the 8-bit data bus.

If you are using a word output port, the lower byte of the word port should be at an even address and the upper byte at an odd address. This is consistent with the organization of the 8088 system memory, as seen in Figure 7.13.

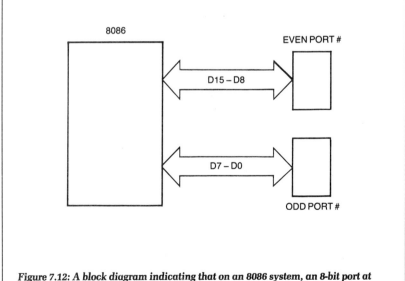

Figure 7.12: A block diagram indicating that on an 8086 system, an 8-bit port at an odd address must connect to the upper data lines (D8–D15), and an 8-bit port at an even address must connect to the lower data lines (D0–D7).

GENERATING A SIGNAL WITH SOFTWARE

Let's now apply the information learned about the 8086/8088 instructions and I/O to various general problems and interfaces used in microcomputer systems. We will start by generating a signal that will turn on or off some piece of hardware, such as a relay.

To generate a signal, the computer must turn an output device on or off. To accomplish this, the computer must change an electrical voltage level in the device from a logical 0 to a logical 1, or from a logical 1 to a logical 0. For example, let us assume that an external relay is connected to bit 0 of an 8-bit output port we will call OUT1. (OUT1 is the variable name representing the address [8 or 16 bits] of the output port.)

To turn the relay on, a logical 1 must be written to bit 0 of OUT1. To turn the relay off, a logical 0 must be written. Here is a program that will turn the relay on:

```
MOV AL,00000001B    B = BINARY
OUT OUT1,AL         OUTPUT 1 TO BIT 0 OF PORT OUT1
```

In this example, we have assumed that the states of the other bit positions of the output port are "don't cares." However, in a normal situation this may not be the case; they may be connected to other relays in the system. In that case, we would not want to change the logical state of these

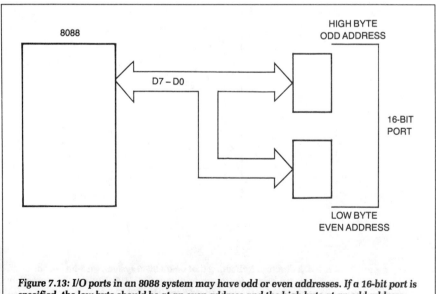

Figure 7.13: I/O ports in an 8088 system may have odd or even addresses. If a 16-bit port is specified, the low byte should be at an even address and the high byte at an odd address.

bits. We can insure that this does not happen by inserting an additional instruction into the program:

```
IN   AL,OUT1        READ THE VALUE OF OUTPUT PORT
OR   AL,00000001B   SET BIT 0 ONLY, ALL OTHER BITS
                    UNCHANGED
OUT  OUT1,AL        OUTPUT TO PORT OUT1
```

This program assumes that we can read the contents of the output port OUT1 or that the contents have been saved in a memory location that we can access. Figure 7.14 shows a block diagram of the concept of turning a relay on and off.

GENERATING A PULSE

We can generate a pulse in the same way that we turn a relay on and off. We first set a bit in an output port to a logical 1, and then reset it to a logical 0 at some finite time later (see Figure 7.15). When the pulse is generated we must keep track of its width with software. To do this, we must generate a computed delay.

DELAY GENERATION

Delays can be generated using software or hardware. For now, let's use software. In a later example, we will generate a hardware delay using a programmable timer. Programmed delays are achieved by counting. To count, a counter register is first loaded with a value, then decremented. The program loops on itself and continues decrementing until the counter reaches the value 0. The total length of time used by this process implements the required delay.

To generate a specific delay, we must know how long each instruction takes to execute at a given clock frequency. An instruction takes a fixed number of clock cycles to execute, and it is this number that must be converted to time, based on the period of the system clock. (*Note:* For this example, we will not be concerned with exact times.)

Let's now generate a delay for the length of time required to decrement the AX register in the loop. Here is the program:

```
      MOV AX,0F45H   LOAD UP AX WITH COUNT
BACK  DEC AX         AX = AX - 1
      JNZ BACK       IF NOT ZERO DEC AGAIN
```

The first instruction line loads the AX register with the immediate value of F45H. The next one, labeled with "BACK," decrements the AX register by one. Following this, the JNZ (jump if not equal to zero) instructions initiates a jump to the instruction line labeled BACK if the result of the decrement is not equal to zero. If the value of the AX register equals zero, the program executes the instruction following the JNZ instruction. A flowchart showing this type of delay appears in Figure 7.16.

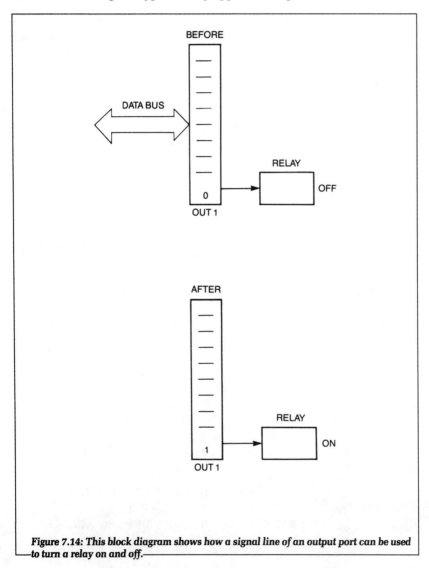

Figure 7.14: This block diagram shows how a signal line of an output port can be used to turn a relay on and off.

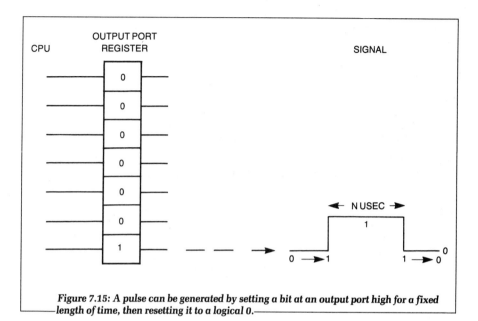

Figure 7.15: A pulse can be generated by setting a bit at an output port high for a fixed length of time, then resetting it to a logical 0.

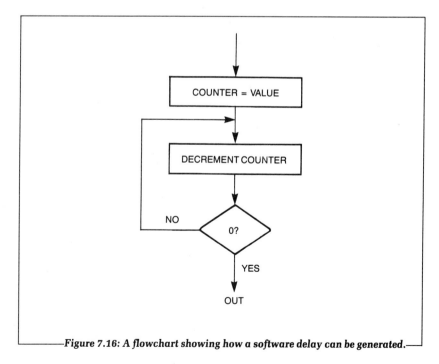

Figure 7.16: A flowchart showing how a software delay can be generated.

Figure 7.17 presents a program for generating a pulse at output port OUT1 bit 0. Note that this program uses the delay program we just described.

LONGER DELAYS

With the 8086/8088 we can easily generate delays using either 8- or 16-bit registers. However, if we need a longer delay time, we can use two 16-bit registers and "nest" decrement loops (as shown in the flowchart in Figure 7.18). A program to realize this flowchart is shown in Figure 7.19.

USING AN 8255 PIO DEVICE WITH THE 8086/8088

We will now show how the 8086/8088 can be used to control the 8255, a programmable input/output device. These devices are often used in a microprocessor system to allow the CPU to electrically control peripheral hardware. We will start with a brief overview of the 8255; we will then proceed to examine some sample software routines written in 8086/8088 assembly language for control of the device.

```
            1 ;
            2 ;    PROGRAM TO GENERATE A DELAY
            3 ;    AX IS USED
            4 ;
            5 ;    OUTPUT PORT OUT1 = 58H
            6 ;    BIT 0 IS THE CONTROL BIT
            7 ;
            8 OUT1     EQU 58H
            9 ;
0000 B001  10    MOV AL,#01        ;SET CONTROL BIT
0002 E658  11    OUT OUT1,AL       ;OUTPUT CONTROL BIT
0004 BB5A04 12   MOV BX,#045AH     ;LOAD BX WITH COUNT VALUE
0007 4B    13    BACK    DEC BX         ;BX = BX – 1
0008 75FD  14    JNZ BACK          ;BX ≠ 0, DEC AGAIN
000A FEC8  15    DEC AL            ;AL = 0
000C E658  16    OUT OUT1,AL       ;CONTROL BIT = 0
           17 ;
           18 ;    PULSE RETURNED TO LOGICAL 0
```

Figure 7.17: This is an 8086/8088 program to generate a pulse using the software delay technique shown in Figure 7.16.

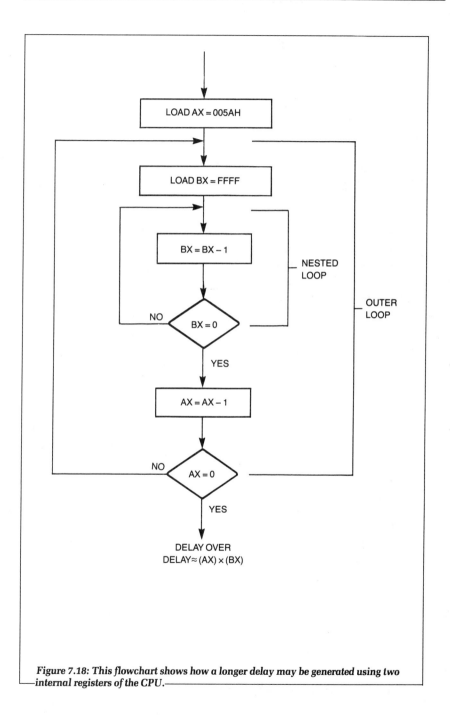

Figure 7.18: This flowchart shows how a longer delay may be generated using two internal registers of the CPU.

OVERVIEW OF THE 8255

The 8255 is a 40-pin, dual in-line package (DIP), LSI device that is designed to perform a variety of interface functions in a microprocessor system environment. Figure 7.20 shows a block diagram of the 8255 device. Let's examine this diagram and discuss in general the function of each block.

In the diagram there are four blocks that physically connect the 8255 to external hardware. These blocks have control lines labeled PA0–PA7, PB0–PB7, PC0–PC3, PC4–PC7. The groups of signals from these blocks are logically divided into three different I/O ports labeled PORTA (PA), PORTB (PB) and PORTC (PC). These four port blocks (PC is divided into two groups) are connected to an internal data bus on the 8255 device. It is via this internal data bus that the ports are programmed.

There are two blocks in Figure 7.20. These blocks, labeled group A control and group B control, define how the three I/O ports are to operate in the system. There are several different operating modes for the 8255, and these must be defined by the CPU writing control words to the device. Notice that group C of the 8255 consists of two 4-bit ports. One of the 4-bit groups is associated with group A and the other with group B device signals.

```
             1  ;
             2  ;   PROGRAM TO GENERATE A DELAY
             3  ;   USING TWO REGISTERS, AX AND BX.
             4  ;   AX IS OUTER LOOP, BX IS INNER LOOP
             5  ;
0000 B85A00  6    MOV AX,#0005AH    ;LOAD UP THE AX REGISTER
0003 BBFFFF  7  BACK    MOV BX,#0FFFFH      ;LOAD UP THE BX REGISTER
0006 4B      8  BACK1    DEC BX                ;BX = BX – 1
0007 75FD    9    JNZ BACK1         ;INNER LOOP ≠ 0
0009 48     10    DEC AX            ;AX = AX – 1
000A 75F7   11    JNZ BACK          ;OUTER LOOP ≠ 0
            12  ;
            13  ;   DELAY LOOP APPROXIMATELY EQUAL TO AX TIMES BX
```

Figure 7.19: This is an 8086/8088 program to realize the delay loop shown in Figure 7.18.

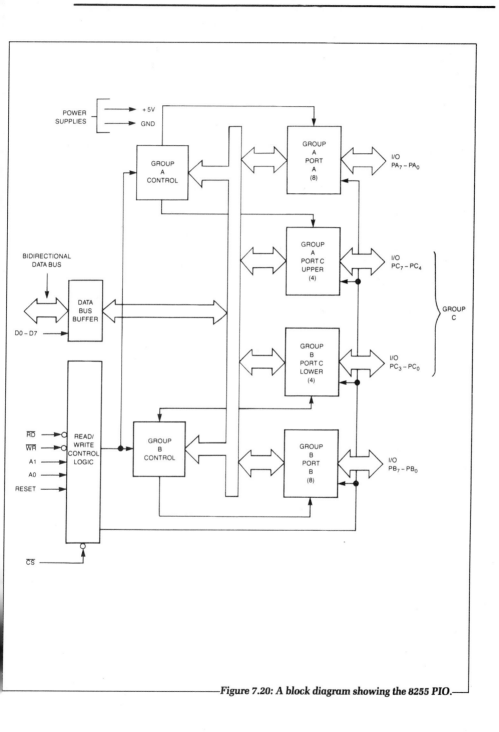

Figure 7.20: A block diagram showing the 8255 PIO.

The final logic blocks in Figure 7.20 are labeled data bus buffer and read/write control logic. These two blocks provide the electrical interface between the 8086/8088 microprocessor and the 8255. The data bus buffer buffers the data input and output lines to and from the CPU data bus. The read/write control logic routes the data to and from the correct internal registers with the appropriate timing. This timing depends on the type of operation being performed by the CPU; that is, it depends on whether or not it is an I/O read or write operation.

PHYSICAL CONNECTION TO THE CPU SYSTEM

Figure 7.21 presents a block diagram that shows how the 8255 is connected to the 8086/8088 system. Note that there are four internal ports accessed by address lines A1 and A0. We will use the port addresses 10H, 11H, 12H, and 13H for the 8088, and 10H, 12H, 14H, and 16H for the 8086. The difference between these two sets of addresses lies in the fact that when an odd address is written to by the 8086, the system transfers the data on the upper data lines (D8–D15). Therefore, when we connect to the lower data lines (D0–D7) of the 8086, all port addresses must be even.

8255 READ AND WRITE REGISTERS

Let's now examine the register definitions and port addresses for the 8255 system shown in Figure 7.21. We will assume that the CPU is an 8088. Here are the register definitions:

PORT #	DEFINITION	DESCRIPTION
10H	Write PORT A data	Output
10H	Read PORT A data	Input
11H	Write PORT B data	Output
11H	Read PORT B data	Input
12H	Write PORT C data	Output
12H	Read PORT C data	Input
13H	Write control word	Output
13H	Illegal read register	

The function of registers 0–2 is defined by the word written to the control register 3 of the 8255. Figure 7.22 shows the bit definitions of the control register. We will be referring to these definitions as we write a program to use the 8255.

BASIC INPUT AND OUTPUT WITH THE 8255

To use the 8255 in the basic I/O mode, the programmer must first write a byte to the control register. This byte defines how the registers of the 8255 device are to be used. The bits of the control register used to program the basic I/O function appear like this:

1	0	0	0	0	0	0	0
D7	D6	D5	D4	D3	D2	D1	D0

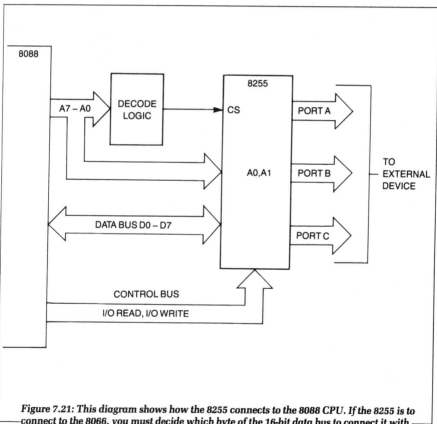

Figure 7.21: This diagram shows how the 8255 connects to the 8088 CPU. If the 8255 is to connect to the 8066, you must decide which byte of the 16-bit data bus to connect it with.

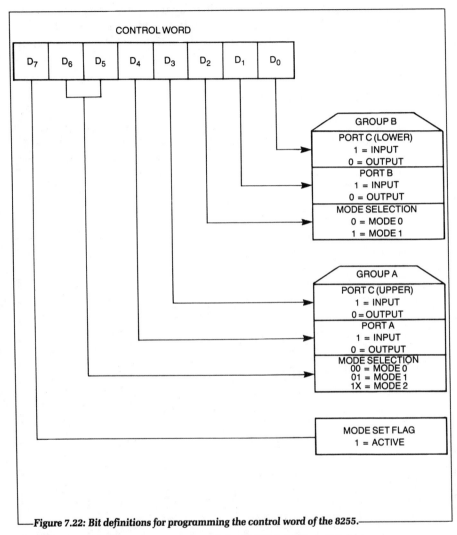

Figure 7.22: Bit definitions for programming the control word of the 8255.

Referring to Figure 7.22 we can see that bit D7 defines this byte as a control word to set the mode of operation. Let's examine each bit:

Bits D6 and D5 define the mode of operation for the 8255 port A.

This will be mode 0.

Bit D4 = 0 indicates that port A is an output.

Bit D3 = 0 sets the upper four bits of port C as outputs.

Bit D2 sets the mode upper for port B. A logical 0 sets mode B as an output port.

Bit D1 = 0 sets port B as an output port.

Bit D0 = 0 sets the lower four bits of port C as an output port.

With this control word written to the 8255, all three ports (A, B, and C) are defined as output ports. This gives the 8255 twenty-four separate output lines to use to interface to external devices. The 8086/8088 instructions for setting up the 8255 in this fashion are:

```
MOV AL,10000000B    CONTROL WORD TO AL
OUT 13H,AL          OUTPUT CONTROL WORD TO 8255
```

Once the 8255 has been programmed with these two instructions, we can simply write data to any output port using the 8086/8088 output instructions. For example, let's suppose we wish to write 23H to port A outputs, 41H to port B outputs, and 73H to port C outputs. To accomplish this, we need an instruction sequence like the following:

```
MOV AL,23H    SET UP PORT A DATA
OUT 10H,AL    OUTPUT DATA TO PORT A
MOV AL,41H    SET UP PORT B DATA
OUT 11H,AL    OUTPUT DATA TO PORT B
MOV AL,73H    SET UP PORT C DATA
OUT 12H,AL    OUTPUT DATA TO PORT C
```

When these instructions are executed, the output ports A, B, and C of the 8255 will be programmed to the specified data values. This is a convenient way to have three individual output ports contained on a single chip.

We could program the ports for a combination of input and output. For example, we could program ports A and C to be output ports, and port B to be an input port. Referring to Figure 7.22, the control word to set up the 8255 in this configuration would be:

```
D7                    D0
 1  0  0  0  0  0  1  0
```

After the control word is programmed into register 3 of the 8255, the device will be logically set up (as shown in Figure 7.23). An IN instruction could be used to read the data input from port B:

```
IN AL,11H    READ DATA FROM PORT B
```

Once the 8255 is set up in the correct configuration, data can be easily read or written at any device port. There are several different combinations for setting up the 8255 in mode 0 basic I/O configuration. So far, we have mentioned only a few.

EXAMPLE OF KEYBOARD SCANNING

As an example of using the 8086/8088 with the 8255, let's now discuss a keyboard interface. Let's assume the keyboard is organized as a 4 × 4 matrix of single-pole single-throw (SPST) switches, and let's use the 8255 to interface the keyboard switches to the 8088. Figure 7.24 shows a block diagram of this system.

Port B outputs are connected to the keyboard columns. Port A inputs are connected to the keyboard rows. The column lines are forced to a logical 0, one at a time. After each column line is set to a logical 0, the input port A is

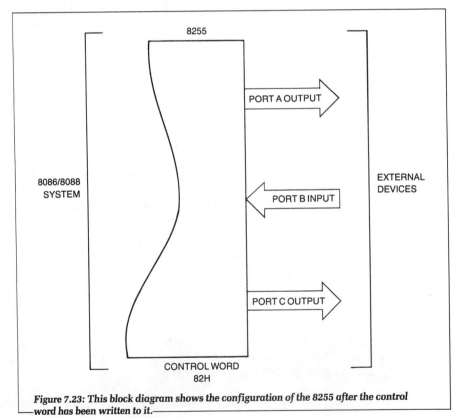

Figure 7.23: *This block diagram shows the configuration of the 8255 after the control word has been written to it.*

read. If any bit read from the input port is a logical 0, a key has been pushed. Based on the column line, which is a logical 0, and the bit in the input port, which is a logical 0, we can tell which key in the matrix has been pressed. Figure 7.25 shows a program that operates in the manner just described.

Although this example was designed for a small (4 × 4) matrix, it can be easily expanded into a matrix of any size. Using an 8255 is an easy way of providing the necessary hardware for the interface.

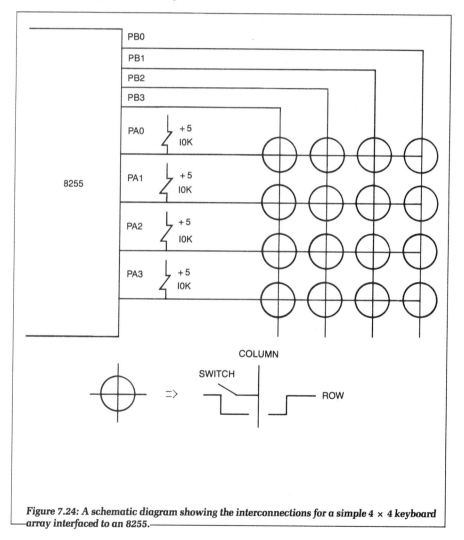

Figure 7.24: A schematic diagram showing the interconnections for a simple 4 × 4 keyboard array interfaced to an 8255.

```
                    1  ;
                    2  ;    PROGRAM FOR DETECTING A KEY PUSH FOR THE
                    3  ;    MATRIX SHOWN IN FIGURE 7-24
                    4  ;
                    5  ;    PORT B IS THE OUTPUT PORT
                    6  ;    PORT A AND C ARE THE INPUT PORTS
                    7  ;
                    8  PORTA    EQU 10H
                    9  PORTB    EQU 11H
                   10  PORTC    EQU 12H
                   11  CONP     EQU 13H        ;CONTROL PORT
                   12  CONWD    EQU 99H        ;CONTROL WORD
                   13  ;
                   14  ;
0000 B099          15           MOV AL,#CONWD    ;LOAD CONWD INTO AL
0002 E613          16           OUT CONP,AL      ;CONWD TO 8255 CONTROL PORT
                   17  ;
0004 BA1100        18           MOV DX,#PORT B   ;DX = ADDRESS OF PORTB
                   19  ;
0007 B3FE          20  COL      MOV BL,#0FEH     ;COLUMN 0 ACTIVE
0009 88D8          21  COL1     MOV AL,BL        ;ACTIVE COLUMN TO AL FOR OUTPUT
000B EE            22           OUT DX,AL        ;ASSERT ACTIVE COLUMN
000C E410          23           IN AL,PORTA      ;READ THE ROW LINES
000E F6D0          24           NOT AL           ;COMPLEMENT INPUT WORD
0010 240F          25           AND AL,#0FH      ;MASK OFF UNUSED BITS
0012 3C00          26           CMP AL,#00H      ;ANY ACTIVE 1'S?
0014 750A          27           JNZ KEYIN        ;IF YES, THEN KEY PUSHED
0016 D0C3          28           ROL BL,1         ;ROTATE ACTIVE COLUMN LEFT BY 1 BIT
0018 80FBEF        29           CMP BL,#0EFH     ;LAST COLUMN ASSERTED?
001B 75EC          30           JNZ COL1         ;NOT LAST COLUMN, ASSERT NEXT ONE
001D E9E7FF        31           JMP COL          ;LAST COLUMN, ASSERT FIRST COLUMN
                   32  ;
                   33  ;    THE FOLLOWING WILL HANDLE A KEY CLOSURE
                   34  ;
0020 88C1          35  KEYIN    MOV CL,AL        ;ROW POS = 1 IN CL REG
0022 88D8          36           MOV AL,BL        ;COLUMN POS IN A REG
0024 F6D0          37           NOT AL           ;COLUMN POS = 1 IN A REG
0026 240F          38           AND AL,#0FH      ;UNUSED BITS = 0
0028 C3            39           RET              ;RETURN FROM SCAN SUBROUTINE
                   40  ;
                   41  ;    RETURN FROM ROUTINE WITH
                   42  ;    AL REG = COLUMN POS, 1 IN ACTIVE COLUMN BIT
                   43  ;    CL REG = ROW POS, 1 IN ACTIVE COLUMN BIT
                   44  ;
```

Figure 7.25: This 8086/8088 program will control the 4 × 4 keyboard matrix shown in Figure 7.24.

PROGRAMMING THE 8253 TIMER CHIP

In this section we will show how the 8086/8088 can be used to control a programmable timer chip. A programmable timer chip is used in many system applications where timing functions are needed. Recall that in an earlier section of this chapter we demonstrated how a pulse can be generated using software. We did this by using the microprocessor in a software loop.

Using a timer chip, the microprocessor only needs to write a few control bytes to set up the timing parameters, and the chip will do the rest of the work. This frees the microprocessor to perform other system tasks.

BLOCK DIAGRAM OF THE 8253 TIMER CHIP

Figure 7.26 shows a block diagram of the 8253. We can see in this figure that there are three independent, programmable counters. Because all the counters are identical, we will not discuss them individually here. Instead, we will concentrate on the programming of a single counter. This information can then be used to program any of the three counters.

An important block in Figure 7.26 is the data bus buffer. This is the logic that buffers the system data bus to and from the microprocessor to the 8253 internal registers. The block that controls the reading and writing of the counter registers is labeled read/write logic.

The final block in Figure 7.26 is labeled control word register. This register contains the programmed information sent to the device from the system microprocessor. In effect this register defines how the device operates logically. Figure 7.27 presents a block diagram showing how the 8253 connects with the 8088 system.

PROGRAMMABLE PULSE GENERATION

Referring to the block diagram in Figure 7.27, we can see that the port addresses for the device are 30H, 31H, 32H, and 33H—where 33H is the control port, and 30H, 31H, and 32H are the counter registers 0, 1, and 2, respectively. Let us now program the 8253 to generate a pulse of a fixed duration under program control. This action is sometimes called a *one-shot*.

In the programmable pulse mode, the 8253 device can be made to give an output pulse that is an integer number of clock pulses. The one-shot will be triggered on the rising edge of the gate input. If the triggers occur during the pulse output, the device will be re-triggered. This is shown in Figure 7.28.

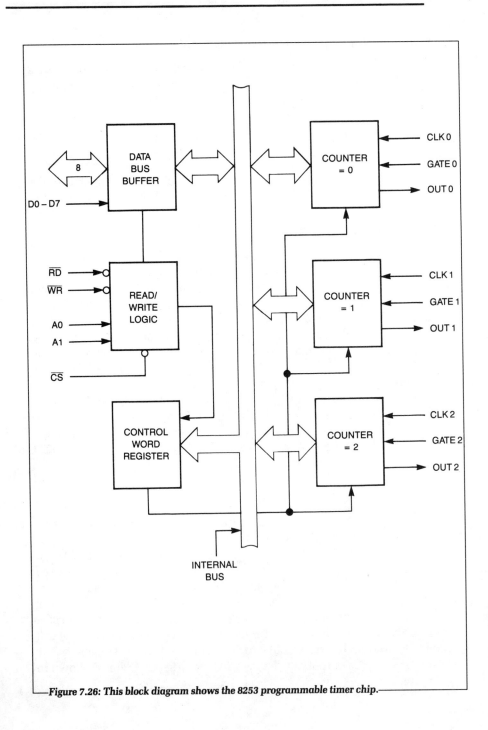

Figure 7.26: This block diagram shows the 8253 programmable timer chip.

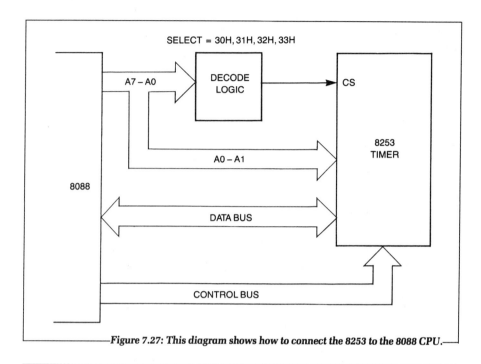

Figure 7.27: This diagram shows how to connect the 8253 to the 8088 CPU.

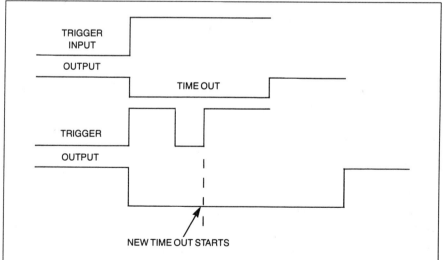

Figure 7.28: This timing diagram shows how the 8253 can be used as a programmable one-shot. When the trigger input goes to a logical 1, the output will go to a logical 0 for the programmed time of the counter. If the trigger is again applied before the counter times out, the time out count will be retriggered.

Let's assume that the input clock frequency to the 8253 is 1 megahertz. We will program the 8253 for an output pulse of exactly 75 microseconds. The 8086/8088 program to perform this setup is shown in Figure 7.29. In this figure, we are assuming that counter #1 is being used as the programmable one-shot.

```
            1 ;
            2 ;   PROGRAM TO SET UP THE 8253
            3 ;   AS A PROGRAMMABLE ONE-SHOT
            4 ;
            5 CNTR1      EQU 31H      ;COUNTER 1 PORT ADDRESS
            6 CONP       EQU 33H      ;CONTROL PORT ADDRESS
            7 ;
0000 B072   8              MOV AL,#72H    ;CONTROL WORD TO AL
0002 E633   9              OUT CONP,AL    ;CONTROL WORD TO 8253
           10 ;
           11 ;   CTR 1, RL = 3, M = 1, BINARY COUNT
           12 ;
0004 B04B  13              MOV AL,#75     ;DECIMAL 75
0006 E631  14              OUT CNTR1,AL   ;NUMBER TO COUNTER 1 LS BYTE
0008 B000  15              MOV AL,#00
000A E631  16              OUT CNTR1,AL   ;OUTPUT TO COUNTER 1 MS BYTE
           17 ;
           18 ;
           19 ;   THE DEVICE IS NOW SET UP WAITING FOR A TRIGGER
           20 ;   INPUT TO THE COUNTER
           21 ;
```

Figure 7.29: An 8086/8088 program for setting up the 8253 as a programmable one-shot with a pulse width of 75 microseconds.

CHAPTER SUMMARY

In this chapter we have presented the essential points of 8086/8088 input and output operations. We began by defining the terms input and output. We then discussed the two 8086/8088 I/O instructions IN and OUT. We learned that each of these instructions can be used in the fixed and variable port mode. Examples were given. Finally, we examined two examples of programming special LSI peripheral chips—chips that are quite common to many 8086/8088 systems. As we described each chip, we examined the port decoding and a block diagram of its connection with the system.

In Chapter 8 we will continue our discussion of 8086/8088 applications and we will write 8088 programs that can be used with the BIOS (Basic Input Output System) of the IBM Personal Computer. Understanding the concepts presented in this chapter will help you in writing the programs for the next chapter.

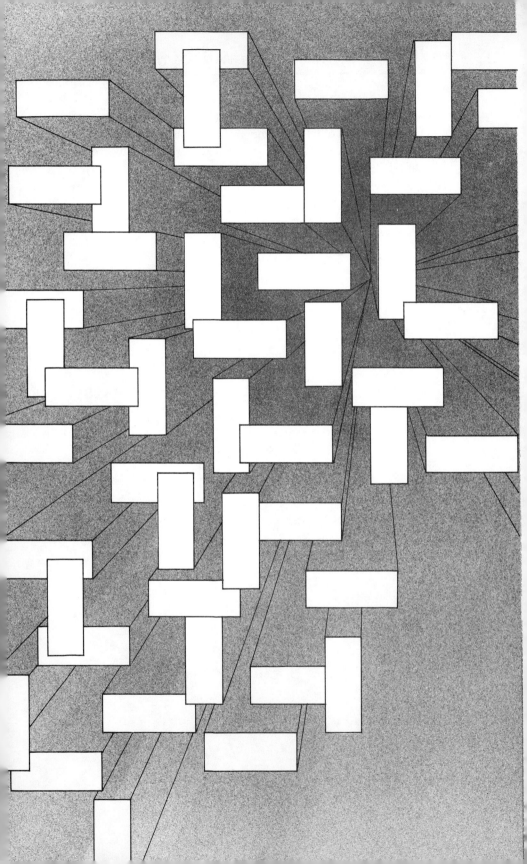

8 MORE APPLICATIONS USING THE IBM PERSONAL COMPUTER

INTRODUCTION

In this chapter we will continue our discussion of useful applications for the 8086/8088. We will prepare two complete software examples. These examples will involve writing code for the IBM Personal Computer—a system that employs the 8088 microprocessor.

BIOS (BASIC I/O SYSTEM)

Before preparing actual assembly language programs, let's turn our attention to some of the details of the IBM PC. In particular, let's examine BIOS, the Basic Input and Output System. The term BIOS is used often in personal computer architecture and literature.

A system BIOS refers to the manner in which the system allows access to the peripheral devices used by the computer. Typical input/output devices are:

1. a floppy or hard disk drive

2. a printer

3. a video display

4. a keyboard input

5. a serial communication link (RS-232) or teletype

Note that every computer has its own unique set of peripheral devices which it controls.

BIOS ADVANTAGE

If we were to examine the hardware interfaces to some of the peripheral devices previously listed, we would find them to be fairly complex. Let's take the floppy disk as an example. To control the hardware of a floppy disk (i.e., the head movement, and the read, write electronics), it is necessary to know the minute details of the interaction between the system software and the system hardware. Such details are necessary for the person writing the code to control the device at the lowest level. However, for the person who is simply interested in using the device, it is an enormous burden to have to learn *all* the intricate details of the system. The BIOS eliminates this step. The BIOS allows the programmer to pass high-level requests (such as reading a file from the disk) and not be burdened with all the details for fulfilling the request (such as checking if the read head is in position, or setting up the parameters for the controller chip). Some controller chip parameters include formatting the data on the disk, specifying single- or double-density storage of data on the disk, etc.

For example, in order to read a sector from a disk, the disk controller chip must be electrically informed of numerous details regarding such things as the configuration of the disk (i.e., how many bytes/sectors are single- or double-sided, etc.). With the BIOS, a programmer can pass a parameter (or binary codes) by simply indicating that a particular sector should be read, and then defining it. The BIOS then processes the request and performs all of the low-level software commands necessary to fulfill the request. See Figure 8.1.

ACCESSING PERIPHERALS USING THE BIOS

Each system has a different technique for accessing the BIOS, which is generally described in the system literature. For the IBM PC, access to the BIOS is through the interrupt structure of the 8088 CPU (discussed in Chapter 6).

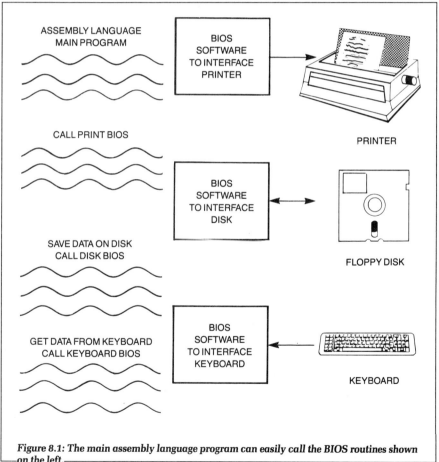

Figure 8.1: The main assembly language program can easily call the BIOS routines shown on the left.

Recall that with the 8086/8088 CPU, interrupts may be generated through hardware and software. In the IBM PC, to access the BIOS routines we can use software to generate interrupts. Each peripheral device that the IBM PC communicates with has one or more interrupt types reserved for accessing it from a program. Figure 8.2 shows the 8088 vector types and the corresponding hardware they access.

INTERRUPT VECTOR (0 – 7F)

ADDRESS HEX	INTERRUPT HEX	FUNCTION
0–3	0	DIVIDE BY ZERO
4–7	1	SINGLE STEP
8–B	2	NON-MASKABLE INTERRUPT (NMI)
C–F	3	BREAK POINT INSTRUCTION ('C'Cx)
10–13	4	OVERFLOW
14–17	5	PRINT SCREEN
18–1F	6,7	RESERVED
20–23	8	TIMER (18.2 PER SECOND)
24–27	9	KEYBOARD INTERRUPT
28–37	A,B,C,D	RESERVED
38–3B	E	DISKETTE INTERRUPT
3C–3F	F	RESERVED
40–43	10	VIDEO I/O CALL
44–47	11	EQUIPMENT CHECK CALL
48–4B	12	MEMORY CHECK CALL
4C–4F	13	DISKETTE I/O CALL
50–53	14	RS232 I/O CALL
54–57	15	CASSETTE I/O CALL
58–5B	16	KEYBOARD I/O CALL
5C–5F	17	PRINTER I/O CALL
60–63	18	ROM BASIC ENTRY MODE
64–67	19	BOOTSTRAP LOADER
68–6B	1A	TIME OF DAY CALL
6C–6F	1B	GET CONTROL ON KEYBOARD BREAK: NOTE 1
70–73	1C	GET CONTROL ON TIMER INTERRUPT: NOTE 1
74–77	1D	POINTER TO VIDEO INITIALIZATION TABLE: NOTE 2
78–7B	1E	POINTER TO DISKETTE PARAMETER TABLE: NOTE 2
7C–7F	1F	POINTER TO TABLE (1B) FOR GRAPHICS CHARACTER GENERATOR FOR ASCII 128–255. DEFAULTS TO 0.0

NOTES: (1) INITIALIZED AT POWER UP TO POINT TO AN IRET INSTRUCTION.
(2) INITIALIZED AT POWER UP TO POINT TO TABLES IN ROM.

Figure 8.2: A list showing the 8088 interrupt table and the corresponding hardware of the IBM PC that these interrupts gain access to.

PASSING PARAMETERS TO A BIOS ROUTINE

When using a routine in the BIOS, very often parameters need to be passed from the calling program to the routine. Such parameters might be data to be printed out, a baud rate being set for an RS-232 communication, or data input from a keyboard —just to name a few. In the IBM BIOS, all parameters are passed to and from the routines via the internal registers of the 8088. Figure 8.3 shows this action in block diagram form.

A question that might arise at this point is "Which registers are used to pass parameters?" Furthermore, "Which parameters are passed?" In answer to these questions we'll examine the documentation of a BIOS routine. Included in this documentation is a section entitled PREAMBLE. The PREAMBLE is the section of the documentation that explains exactly

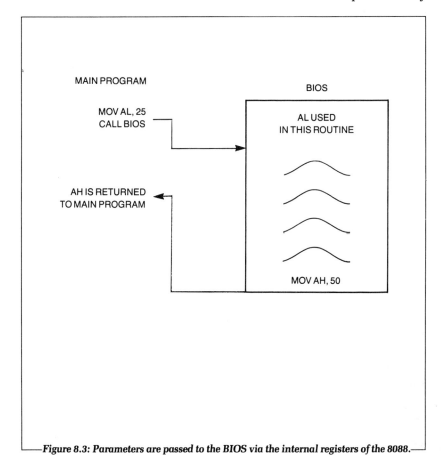

Figure 8.3: Parameters are passed to the BIOS via the internal registers of the 8088.

which parameters are passed and within what parameters. To learn more about the PREAMBLE, let's examine the following example.

PREAMBLE FOR THE PRINTER I/O

START OF PREAMBLE

The following routine provides communication with the printer.

(AH) = 0 Print the character in (AL).

On return from this routine, AH = 1 if the character could not be printed; that is, if a time out was reached. The other bits are set as in a normal status call.

(AH) = 1 Initialize the printer port.

On return, AH is set with printer status.

(AH) = 2 Read the printer status into (AH).

The bit definitions for the printer status are:

D7 = 1 indicates printer is busy.

D6 = 1 is the acknowledge bit.

D5 = 1 means the printer is out of paper.

D4 = 1 indicates the printer is selected.

D3 = 1 indicates an I/O error.

D2 =   unused.

D1 =   unused.

D0 = 1 is an indication of a time out.

END OF PREAMBLE*

From this PREAMBLE of the printer BIOS, we can see that when a routine is called via the correct software interrupt, the AH register will direct

---

*Adapted from *Personal Computer Hardware Reference Library: Technical Reference.* Copyright© International Business Machines Corporation.

the routine action. Therefore, we must insure that the AH register is set prior to calling the routine.

When we return from the routine, the calling program can test the value of the AH register to logically indicate the status of the printer, that is, whether or not the routine has performed its intended function.

A FIRST EXAMPLE: USING THE PRINTER BIOS ROUTINE

In this example, we will write an 8088 assembly language routine that uses the PRINTER BIOS just described.

DESCRIPTION OF THE PROBLEM

Before we write the actual program for using the printer BIOS, let's discuss the problem to be solved. In this particular application we want to print data stored in a software buffer. This data will be formed in the main program. When the buffer is full, it will be sent to the printer BIOS to be printed out.

In this example, we will assume that the buffer has been filled, and we will show only the software required to print it. The memory location for the first element in the BUFFER will be labeled BUF_START. The last data in the buffer will be equal to 00H (or when the number of characters equals 80 decimal). A flowchart for this program appears in the next section.

FLOWCHART FOR THE PROBLEM

Figure 8.4 shows a flowchart for one solution to this problem.

8088 PROGRAM TO REALIZE THE FLOWCHART

Figure 8.5 shows an 8088 program that will implement the flowchart given in Figure 8.4. Let's examine it so that we completely understand what each instruction is used for. Before we begin, however, note that all of the steps referenced in the flowchart of Figure 8.4 are shown in the program. This helps you to see how each step of the flowchart is realized with 8088 mnemonics. The mnemonics shown in Figure 8.5 are for an 8088 assembler only. Some of the expressions and number indicators may vary if you are using an assembler by a different manufacturer.

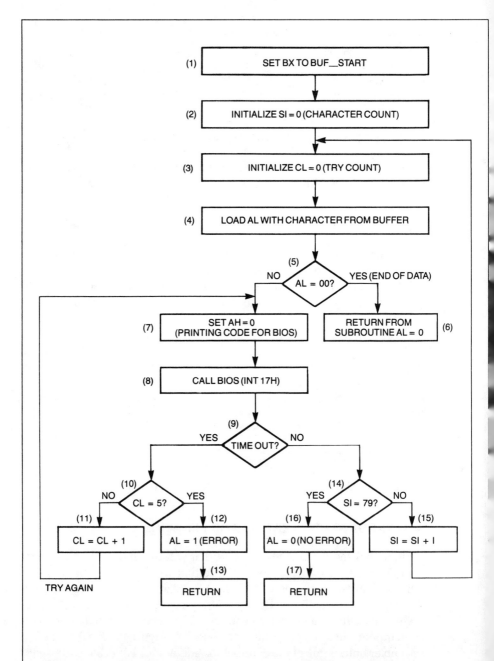

Figure 8.4: A flowchart for printing a buffer full of data using the printer BIOS.

```
                       1
                       2  ;;;;;;;;;;;;;;;;;;;;;;;;;;;;;;;;;;;;;;;;;;;;;;;;;;;;;;;;;;;;;;;;;;;;;;;;;;;;;;;;;;;;
                       3  ;
                       4  ;   EXAMPLE ROUTINE FOR USING THE PRINTER
                       5  ;   BIOS ON THE IBM PC.
                       6  ;
                       7  ;   REG BX = STARTING LOC OF BUFFER TO PRINT
                       8  ;       SI = CHARACTER COUNT
                       9  ;       CL = NUMBER OF TRYS, MAX OF 5
                      10  ;       AL = CHARACTER TO BE PRINTED PASSED TO BIOS
                      11  ;       AH = PRINT CODE 0–2 PASSED TO BIOS
                      12  ;
                      13  ;       RETURN FROM SUBROUTINE WITH AL = 0, NO ERROR
                      14  ;       AL = 1, ERROR. THIS WILL BE CHECKED IN MAIN
                      15  ;       PROGRAM
                      16  ;
                      17  ;;;;;;;;;;;;;;;;;;;;;;;;;;;;;;;;;;;;;;;;;;;;;;;;;;;;;;;;;;;;;;;;;;;;;;;;;;;;;;;;;;;;
                      18  ;
                      19  ;   SET ORIGIN OF SUBROUTINE TO 0B00H
                      20  ;
                      21              ORG 0B00H        ;SET ORIGIN
                      22  ;
                      23  ;  STEP 1
                      24  ;
0B00 B25B320B         25              MOV BX,#BUF__START    ;SET ADDRESS OF BUF IN BX
                      26  ;
                      27  ;  STEP 2
                      28  ;
0B03 BE0000           29              MOV SI,#0000H         ;SET CHARACTER COUNT = 0
                      30  ;
                      31  ;  STEP 3
                      32  ;
0B06 B100             33  STFP3    MOV CL,#00H          ;SET TRY COUNT = 0
                      34  ;
                      35  ;  STEP 4
                      36  ;
0B08 8A00             37              MOV AL,[BX,SI]       ;LOAD AL WITH CHARACTER
                      38  ;
                      39  ;  STEP 5
                      40  ;
0B0A 3C00             41              CMP AL,#00H          ;LAST DATA ????
0B0C 7501             42              JNZ STEP7            ;IF NO THEN GO TO STEP 7
                      43  ;
                      44  ;  STEP 6    END OF DATA, RETURN WITH AL = 0, NO ERROR
                      45  ;
0B0E C3               46              RET                  ;AL = 0, RETURN
                      47  ;
```

Figure 8.5: An 8088 program to realize the flowchart shown in Figure 8.4.

```
                48  ;   STEP 7    SET THE PRINT CODE FOR BIOS = 0
                49  ;
0B0F B400       50  STEP7    MOV AH,#00
                51  ;
                52  ;   STEP 8
                53  ;
0B11 CD17       54           INT 17H                 CALL BIOS ROUTINE
                55  ;
                56  ;   STEP 9
                57  ;
0B13 80E401     58           AND AH,#01H             ;CHECK FOR TIMEOUT
0B16 740D       59           JZ  STEP14              ;  GOOD TRANSFER
                60  ;
                61  ;   STEP 10    A TIMEOUT WAS RETURNED FROM THE BIOS
                62  ;
0B18 80F905     63           CMP CL,#5               ;FIVE TRIES YET????
0B1B 7405       64           JZ  STEP12              ;  YES MUST RETURN WITH ERROR
                65  ;
                66  ;   STEP 11    HAVE NOT TRIED 5 TIMES YET
                67  ;
0B1D FEC1       68           INC CL                  ;BUMP TRY COUNT
0B1F E9EDFF     69           JMP STEP7               ;DO IT AGAIN
                70  ;
                71  ;   STEP 12    HAD AN ERROR MUST RETURN WITH AL = 1
                72  ;
0B22 B001       73  STEP12   MOV AL,#1
                74  ;
                75  ;   STEP 13
                76  ;
0B24 C3         77           RET                     ;RETURN TO MAIN PROGRAM
                78  ;
                79  ;   STEP 14    NO TIMEOUT, CHARACTER WAS PRINTED OK.
                80  ;
0B25 81FE4F00   81  STEP14   CMP SI,#79              ;LAST CHARACTER????
0B29 7404       82  JZ STEP 16   ;YES, RETURN WITH AL = 0
                83  ;
                84  ;   STEP 15
                85  ;
0B2B 46         86           INC SI                  ;BUMP THE CHARACTER COUNT
0B2C E9D7FF     87           JMP STEP3               ;PRINT THE NEXT CHARACTER
                88  ;
                89  ;   STEP 16    RETURN WITH NO ERROR, GOOD BUFFER PRINT
                90  ;
0B2F B000       91  STEP16   MOV AL,#0
```

Figure 8.5: An 8088 program to realize the flowchart shown in Figure 8.4, continued.

```
                  92  ;
                  93  ;  STEP 17 RETURN
                  94  ;
0B31 C3           95          RET
                  96  ;
                  97  ;  THE PRINT BUFFER IS LOCATED IMMEDIATELY AFTER
                  98  ;  THIS ROUTINE
                  99  ;
                  100 BUF_START    RSV 80    ;RESERVE 80 LOCATIONS FOR BUFFER
                  101 ;
0B82 90           102         NOP


TOTAL ERRORS:              0


SYMBOL          VALUE          LINE #

BUF_START       B32             100
STEP12          B22              73
STEP14          B25              81
STEP16          B2F              91
STEP3           B06              33
STEP7           B0F              50
```

Figure 8.5: An 8088 program to realize the flowchart shown in Figure 8.4, continued.

Step 1   In this step the address of the buffer (computed at the time of assembly) is moved into the BX register. BUF_START is a label at the end of the program. The addressing mode is immediate; that is, the address value, rather than the data located at the memory address, is moved into the BX register.

Steps 2 and 3   In steps 2 and 3, the character count in the SI register and the number-of-tries count in the CL register are set to zero. The character count keeps track of the position in the buffer of the character being printed. A maximum value of 79 is used for this register. This is due to the fact that the count starts at zero.

The number-of-tries register (CL) is used when a time out error is returned from the BIOS routine. A maximum of five tries is attempted to print the character. At the end of five tries, if there has not been a successful print, the subroutine will return to the main program with the AL register set to 1, thus indicating an error in the print routine.

Step 4   In this step the character is moved from the buffer into the AL register. Note that the addressing mode will be indirect with a base, plus index. The base register is BX and the index register is SI. Recall that SI is the character count and BX is the starting address of the buffer.

Step 5   In step 5, we examine the data that was in the buffer. If the data equals 00, it signifies the end of the data to print and we return from the subroutine (Step 6) with AL = 0, thus indicating a successful buffer print. If AL does not equal 00, the character is printed (Step 7).

Step 6   In this step, we return to the main program from this subroutine. It should be noted that this return is a NEAR intra-segment return. A NEAR intra-segment return determines how data is popped off the stack. See Chapter 5.

Steps 7 and 8   These two steps set the print code for the BIOS routine and then call the routine. The call is accomplished via the INT 17H. This is a software interrupt.

Step 9   When the program reaches this point, it has returned from the BIOS. We will mask off the upper bits of the AH register in order to check the time out bit D0 for a logical 1. If this bit is a logical 0, we proceed to step 14. If it is a logical 1, a time out error has been returned. If this is the case, we proceed to step 10.

Steps 10 and 11   These steps are used to check if we have tried to print the same character five times. If we have, then we go on to step 12. If we have not, we jump back to step 7, after incrementing the CL register. The character to print is still in the AL register. Only the AH register must be reinitialized prior to calling the BIOS routine. This is due to the fact that the printer BIOS routine will change the contents of AH only.

Steps 12 and 13   At step 12, we load the AL register with 01. This indicates to the main calling program that there was an error in the buffer print routine. Step 13 returns to the main program.

Step 14   If we reach step 14, a single character has been printed successfully by the printer BIOS. We now check to see whether or not this was the last character to be printed; that is, does SI = 79? If this character is equal to 79, the last character in the buffer has been printed and we jump to step 16 and set the AL register equal to 0. The zero indicates that a successful print buffer has occurred.

Step 15   Step 15 increments the SI register to point to the next character in the buffer to be printed. After incrementing the pointer, the program will jump to step 3.

Steps 16 and 17   These two steps set the AL register equal to zero and then return to the main program. A zero in the AL register indicates that the buffer print was successful.

PRINT BUFFER

At the end of the subroutine shown in Figure 8.5, we can see that the print buffer has reserved 80 bytes. The buffer starts at the memory address 0B32H, which is the address immediately after the RET instruction. The end of the buffer is at memory address 0B81H, which is 0B32H + 79 decimal, which comes to 80 total locations. The starting address of the print buffer is labeled BUF__START.

Note that the symbol table appears at the end of the program.

ANOTHER EXAMPLE USING THE KEYBOARD AND RS-232 BIOS

Let's look at a second example. In this example, we will prepare a program that uses both the RS-232 and the keyboard BIOS. This program will input a key stroke from the keyboard and output it over the RS-232 communication line. This type of application program could be used as part of a larger program that would enable the IBM PC to act as a stand-alone terminal.

In such an application you would receive characters from the RS-232 port and display them on the video screen of the terminal. Figure 8.6 shows a block diagram of the routines necessary to use the IBM PC as a stand-alone terminal.

Figure 8.7 shows a block diagram of the two operations we will be performing in this particular 8088 programming application.

KEYBOARD PREAMBLE

Before we can make use of the keyboard BIOS, we must understand how parameters are passed and sent to the routine. This information is

IBM SYSTEM AS A STAND-ALONE TERMINAL

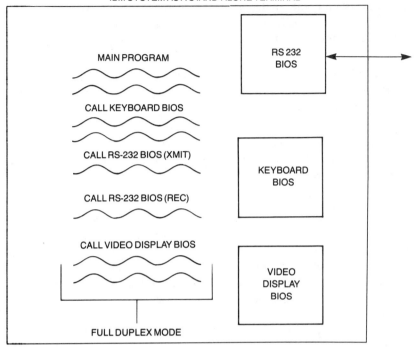

—*Figure 8.6: To use the IBM PC as a stand-alone terminal, you will need to use the*——— *BIOS routine shown above.*

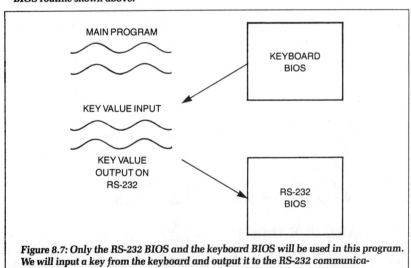

Figure 8.7: Only the RS-232 BIOS and the keyboard BIOS will be used in this program. We will input a key from the keyboard and output it to the RS-232 communica- ——*tion board.*———————————————

given in the PREAMBLE of the keyboard BIOS, as shown below:

START OF PREAMBLE

Keyboard I/O INT 16H

(AH) = 0   reads the next ASCII character struck from the keyboard; then returns the result in AL; and returns the scan code in AH.

(AH) = 1   sets the Z flag to indicate if an ASCII character is available to read.

(ZF) = 1   indicates that no code is available.

(ZF) = 0   indicates that no code is available. If ZF equals 0, the next character in the buffer to be read is in AX, and the entry remains in the buffer.

(AH) = 2   returns the current shift status in the AL register. The bit settings for this code are indicated in the equates for the KB_flag. These bit settings are:

INS_STATE   EQU 80H;   INSERT STATE IS ACTIVE

CAPS_STATE   EQU 40H;   CAPS LOCK STATE HAS
                          BEEN TOGGLED

NUM_STATE   EQU 20H;   NUM LOCK STATE HAS
                          BEEN TOGGLED

SCROLL_STATE EQU 10H;   SCROLL LOCK STATE HAS
                          BEEN TOGGLED

CTL_SHIFT   EQU 04H;   CONTROL SHIFT KEY HAS
                          BEEN DEPRESSED

LEFT_SHIFT   EQU 02H;   LEFT SHIFT KEY HAS
                          BEEN DEPRESSED

RIGHT_SHIFT   EQU 01H;   RIGHT SHIFT KEY HAS
                          BEEN DEPRESSED

Only the AX register and the flags are affected by this routine. All other registers are retained.

END OF KEYBOARD PREAMBLE*

Using this preamble, we are able to use the keyboard routine for inputting a keystroke.

*Adapted from *Personal Computer Hardware Reference Library: Technical Reference.* Copyright© International Business Machines Corporation.

RS-232 PREAMBLE

We will use the RS-232 BIOS in this example. Here is the preamble for the RS-232 BIOS.

START OF RS-232 PREAMBLE
___

RS232__IO INT 14H

This routine provides byte stream I/O to the communications port according to the parameters:

(AH) = 0   Initialize the communications port. AL contains the bits for initialization. These bits are defined as:

BITS	7,6,5	Baud Rate
	0 0 0	110
	0 0 1	150
	0 1 0	300
	0 1 1	600
	1 0 0	1200
	1 0 1	2400
	1 1 0	4800
	1 1 1	9600

BITS	4,3	Parity
	X 0	none
	0 1	odd
	1 1	even

BIT   2 stop bits
        0 1 stop bit
        1 2 stop bits

BITS	1,0	word length
	1 0	7 bits
	1 1	8 bits

On return from a routine with AH = 0, the conditions are set as in a call to commo (communication) status (AH = 3) as shown below.

(AH = 1)   sends the character in (AL) over the commo line. The AL register is preserved.

On exit, bit 7 of AH is set if the routine was unable to transmit the byte of data over the line. The remainder of AH is set as in a status request, thus reflecting the status of the line.

>   (AH = 2)   receives a character in (AL) from the commo line, before returning to the caller.

On exit from this routine, AH has the current line status, as set by the status routine, except that the only bits left on (or that are value) are the error bits (7,4,3,2,1). In this case, the time out bit indicates that the data set ready was not received. AH is non-zero only when an error has occurred.

>   (AH) = 3   returns the commo port status in (AX).

AH contains the line control status:

>   bit 7 = time out

>   bit 6 = trans shift register empty

>   bit 5 = trans holding register empty

>   bit 4 = break detect

>   bit 3 = framing error

>   bit 2 = parity error

>   bit 1 = overrun error

>   bit 0 = data ready

AL contains the modem status:

>   bit 7 = received line signal detect

>   bit 6 = ring indicator

>   bit 5 = data set ready

>   bit 4 = clear to send

>   bit 3 = delta receive line signal detect

>   bit 2 = trailing edge ring detector

>   bit 1 = delta data set ready

>   bit 0 = delta clear to send

AX is modified according to the parameters of the call. All other registers are unchanged.
END OF RS-232 PREAMBLE*

PROGRAM DEFINITION

Using the preambles given for the RS-232 and the keyboard BIOS, let's now write an 8088 program to read a character from the keyboard and transmit it over the RS-232 communication line. The program will terminate when a semicolon is typed at the keyboard.

The data will be transmitted to another system with the following serial transmission parameters:

    baud rate   = 2400

    parity   = odd

    stop bit   = 2 bits

    word length = 8 bits

These parameters will be set up with the IBM PC RS-232 port, prior to the transmission of any characters.

FLOWCHART FOR THE PROGRAM

Figure 8.8 shows a flowchart for this program. Let's discuss this flowchart before we realize it with 8088 software. The first step is to initialize the RS-232 port.

Next, the program calls the keyboard BIOS. When a key is returned from the BIOS, it is sent to the RS-232 BIOS. At this point the character is transmitted out of the IBM PC over the RS-232 bus. In the transmit loop of the flowchart, we will try to transmit the character up to 10 times. If the character has not been successfully transmitted after 10 tries, an error code will be set.

To terminate the program, type a semicolon. The flowchart of Figure 8.6 checks for a semicolon, prior to transmission.

8088 PROGRAM

A complete, assembled 8088 program to realize the flowchart of Figure 8.8 is shown in Figure 8.9.

---

*Adapted from *Personal Computer Hardware Reference Library: Technical Reference*. Copyright© International Business Machines Corporation.

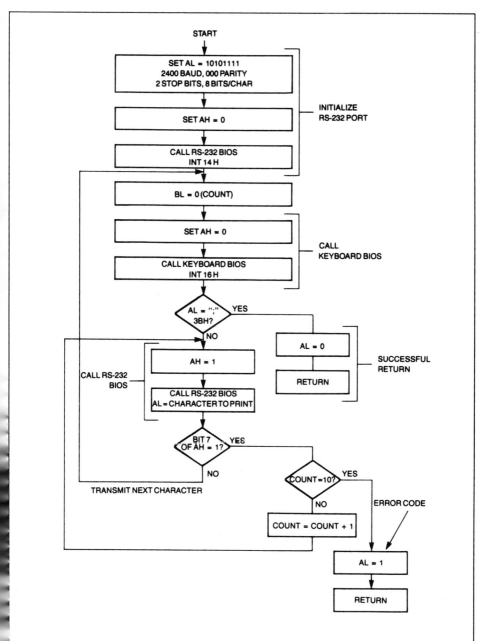

Figure 8.8: A flowchart for reading a character from the keyboard and then sending the character over the RS-232 communication line.

```
  1  ;;;;;;;;;;;;;;;;;;;;;;;;;;;;;;;;;;;;;;;;;;;;;;;;;;;;;;;;;;;;;;;;;;;;;;;;;;;;;;;;;;;;;;
  2  ;
  3  ;   SUBROUTINE TO USE THE KEYBOARD AND RS-232
  4  ;   BIOS FOR THE IBM PERSONAL COMPUTER
  5  ;   KEYBOARD BIOS = INT 16H
  6  ;   RS-232 BIOS    = INT 14H
  7  ;
  8  ;   BL = NUMBER OF TIMES TO XMIT BEFORE ERROR
  9  ;
 10  ;   AL RETURNED = 0, NO ERROR IN XMISSION
 11  ;   AL RETURNED = 1, ERROR IN XMISSION
 12  ;
 13  ;   THE SUBROUTINE WILL READ A CHARACTER FROM THE
 14  ;   KEYBOARD AND THEN XMIT THE CHARACTER OVER THE
 15  ;   RS-232 BUS. A SEMICOLON WILL TERMINATE THE
 16  ;   SUBROUTINE
 17  ;
 18  ;;;;;;;;;;;;;;;;;;;;;;;;;;;;;;;;;;;;;;;;;;;;;;;;;;;;;;;;;;;;;;;;;;;;;;;;;;;;;;;;;;;;;;
 19  ;
 20        ORG 0B00H
 21  ;
 22  ;EQUATES FOR THE SUBROUTINE
 23  ;
 24  RS__232 EQU    14H       ;INTERRUPT TYPE FOR RS-232
 25  KEY__BOARD   EQU 16H ;INTERRUPT TYPE FOR KEYBOARD
 26  MAX__COUNT   EQU 10   ;MAXIMUM NUMBER OF TRIES TO XMIT
 27  SEMI__COLON  EQU 3BH ;ASCII FOR SEMICOLON
 28  ;
 29  ;;;;;;;;;;;;;;;;;;;;;;;;;;;;;;;;;;;;;;;;;;;;;;;;;;;;;;;;;;;;;;;;;;;;;;;;;;;;;;;;;;;;;;
 30  ;
 31  ;   INITIALIZE THE RS-232 PORT
 32  ;
```

```
0B00 B0AF  33         MOV AL,#10101111P  ;2400 BAUD,ODD PARITY
           34  ;                          2 STOP BITS, 8 BITS/CHAR
0B02 B400  35         MOV AH,#00         ;SET CODE FOR RS-232
0B04 CD14  36    INT RS__232            ;CALL RS-232 BIOS
           37  ;
           38  ;      NOW TO READ THE KEYBOARD CHARACTER
           39  ;
           40  ;      FIRST INITIALIZE THE XMIT COUNT
           41  ;
0B06 B300  42  GO1 MOV BL,#00            ;COUNT = 0
0B08 B400  43      MOV AH,#00            ;CODE FOR KEYBOARD BIOS
0B0A CD16  44      INT KEY__BOARD        ;CALL KEYBOARD BIOS
           45  ;
           46  ;      CHECK FOR SEMICOLON
           47  ;
```

Figure 8.9: An 8088 program to realize the flowchart shown in Figure 8.8.

```
   0B0C 3C3B    48      CMP AL,#SEMI_COLON      ;CHECK FOR SEMICOLON TO END
   0B0E 7503    49              JNZ TRANSMIT    ;NOT EQUAL END THE CHAR
                50  ;
                51  ;   IF A SEMICOLON STOP      PROGRAM
                52  ;
   0B10 B000    53              MOV AL,#00       ;SET AL = 0, INDICATES NO ERROR
   0B12 C3      54              RET              ;RETURN TO MAIN PROGRAM
                55  ;
                56  ;   TRANSMIT SECTION OF SUBROUTINE
                57  ;
   0B13 B401    58  TRANSMIT    MOV AH,#01H      ;SET CODE FOR RS-232 BIOS
   0B15 CD14    59              INT RS_232       ;CALL RS-232 BIOS
   0B17 F6C480  60              TEST AH,#80H     ;BIT 7 SET??
   0B1A 74EA    61              JZ GO1           ;NOT SET, LOOP AGAIN
                62  ;
                63  ;   AT THIS POINT, THE CHARACTER WAS NOT ABLE TO XMIT
                64  ;
0B1C 80FB0A     65              CMP BL,#MAX_COUNT ;TEN TRIES YET??
0B1F 7405       66              JZ ERROR_END      ;YES, RETURN WITH ERROR
0B21 FEC3       67              INC BL            ;BUMP TRY COUNT
0B23 E9EDFF     68              JMP TRANSMIT      ;TRANSMIT AGAIN
                69  ;
                70  ; ERROR RETURN SECTION
                71  ;
0B26 B001       72  ERROR_END   MOV AL,#01H  ;SET ERROR CODE
0B28 C3         73              RET          ;RETURN TO MAIN PROGRAM
                74  ;

TOTAL ERRORS:               0

SYMBOL        VALUE           LINE#
_____
ERROR_END                   B26    72
GO1           B06                   42
KEY_BOARD                   16             25
MAX_COUNT                   A              26
RS_232        14                    24
SEMI_COLON                  3B             27
TRANSMIT                    B13            58
```

Figure 8.9: An 8088 program to realize the flowchart shown in Figure 8.8, continued.

CHAPTER SUMMARY

In this chapter we have shown two complete examples of application programs involving the 8088 CPU. These programs have made use of the special BIOS (Basic Input and Output System) contained in the IBM PC. If you have access to an IBM PC, these examples should help you get started in writing your own 8086/8088 applications programs.

9 PROGRAM DEVELOPMENT

INTRODUCTION

So far in this text, we have examined the internal architecture of the CPU; we have discussed the use of the 8086/8088 instruction set; and we have shown examples of programs in assembled form. In this final chapter, we will discuss the important topic of program development. There are several levels of hardware and software resources to consider when developing programs. Determining the appropriate level depends on the individual application. In this chapter, we will present and evaluate different available resources.

PROGRAMMING CHOICES

A program may be written in binary or hexadecimal, an assembly-level language, or a high-level language. Figure 9.1 shows the different levels of programming. Let's discuss them.

HEXADECIMAL CODING

Some programs are written using assembly-level mnemonics. The actual translation of such mnemonics into the corresponding binary code requires an assembler. When there is no assembler, the translation must be done by hand. Because translation into binary is tedious and error-prone, users often use hexadecimal code instead. There are some single-board microcomputers that will only accept programs entered in hexadecimal

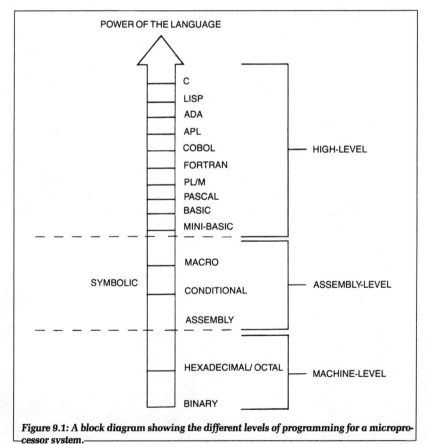

Figure 9.1: A block diagram showing the different levels of programming for a microprocessor system.

code. Generally, translating instructions into the corresponding code is only reasonable for a small number of instructions—and this number varies from programmer to programmer.

In summary, hexadecimal coding is not a desirable way to enter a program into a computer—it is simply an economical one. The cost of an assembler and the required alphanumeric keyboard is traded-off against the increased time and effort required to enter the program in the system memory. Therefore, if it is necessary to use hexadecimal coding, it is wise to first write the program in assembly-language mnemonics, then convert it into hexadecimal code. This is because a program written in assembly language is easier to understand and debug.

ASSEMBLY-LANGUAGE PROGRAMMING

Assembly-level or assembly-language programming includes both those programs entered into the system in hexadecimal form and those entered in symbolic assembly-level form. We will now examine the direct entry of a program in its assembly language representation.

When a program in assembly language is entered, there must be an assembler program available that will read the mnemonic instructions of the program. The purpose of an assembler is to translate the instructions into the required bit patterns, using 1 to 6 bytes, as specified by the encoding of the instructions. A good assembler also offers a number of additional facilities for writing a program.

Later on in this chapter, we will review the various software resources normally available on a system. But first, let's examine the third programming alternative: high-level language programming.

HIGH-LEVEL LANGUAGE PROGRAMMING

An 8086/8088 program may also be written in a high-level language, such as BASIC, PL/M-86, or Pascal, to name a few. A high-level language offers powerful instructions that make programming faster and easier than with assembly language. But high-level instructions must be translated by a complex program inside the computer into the final binary representation that a microcomputer can execute.

Typically, each high-level instruction is translated into many individual binary instructions by a program called a compiler, or by an interpreter. A *compiler* translates all the instructions of a program into object code. By contrast, an *interpreter* interprets a single instruction, executes it, and then translates the next one and executes it.

The BASIC language uses an interpreter, while the Pascal language uses a compiler. An interpreter offers the advantage of interactive response. This enables the programmer to check the instructions, one at a time, while entering them into the computer. Further, a single instruction may be executed as soon as it is entered into the computer. A disadvantage of an interpreter is the speed at which it executes instructions. A compiled program runs much faster than an interpreted one—the speed difference does, however, vary from system to system.

SOFTWARE SUPPORT

Let's begin our examination of software support by reviewing the main software facilities available in a complete system. As we proceed, we will summarize the definitions we introduced previously. Furthermore, we will define important programs available in a software development system.

Let's begin with the assembler. The *assembler* translates the mnemonic representation of instructions into their binary equivalent. It normally translates one symbolic instruction into one binary instruction, which occupies from one to six bytes of data. The resulting binary code, called the *object code*, is directly executable by the microcomputer. An assembler will also produce a complete mnemonic listing as well as a symbol definition list of the program, as shown in Figure 9.2. An assembler will also list syntax errors, such as misspelled or illegal instructions, branching errors, or duplicate or missing labels.

The *monitor* is the main program for using the hardware resources of the system. It continuously monitors the input devices for input; in addition, it manages the reset of the devices. As an example, a minimal monitor for a single-board microcomputer equipped with a keyboard and LEDs will continuously scan the keyboard for user inputs. When inputs are detected, the monitor will display the appropriate alphanumeric data on the LED readouts.

In addition to the previously mentioned tasks, the monitor program must recognize a number of limited commands from the keyboard. Examples of these commands are commands that start, stop, continue, load memory, or examine memory. On a large system that provides complex file management or task scheduling, the monitor is often qualified as the executive program. The overall set of facilities is called the *operating system*. If the files reside on disk, the operating system may be called a disk operating system (or DOS).

An *editor* facilitates the entry and modification of text or programs. It allows the user to conveniently enter, append, and insert characters in the text. Furthermore, the editor enables the user to add and remove lines of text, as well as search for characters or strings. The editor is an important resource for convenient and effective text entry of source code.

The term *debugger* refers to a facility used in debugging programs. If a program does not work properly the first time, a debugger may prove useful. It allows the user to insert breakpoints to suspend execution of a program at specified addresses in order to examine registers and/or memory locations.

A *loader* or *linking loader* places various blocks of object code at specified positions in the memory and adjusts their respective symbolic pointers, so that they can reference each other.

A *simulator* or an *emulator* program simulates the operation of a

```
           1  ;
           2  ;   PROGRAM TO SET UP THE 8253
           3  ;   AS A PROGRAMMABLE ONE-SHOT
           4  ;
           5  CNTR1       EQU 31H        ;COUNTER 1 PORT ADDRESS
           6  CONP        EQU 33H        ;CONTROL PORT ADDRESS
           7  ;
0000 B072  8               MOV AL,#72H    ;CONTROL WORD TO AL
0002 E633  9               OUT CONP,AL    ;CONTROL WORD TO 8253
          10  ;
          11  ;   CTR 1, RL = 3, M = 1, BINARY COUNT
          12  ;
0004 B04B 13               MOV AL,#75     ;DECIMAL 75
0006 E631 14               OUT CNTR1,AL   ;NUMBER TO COUNTER 1 LS BYTE
0008 B000 15               MOV AL,#00
000A E631 16               OUT CNTR1,AL   ;OUTPUT TO COUNTER 1 MS BYTE
          17
          18  ;
          19  ;   THE DEVICE IS NOW SET UP WAITING FOR A TRIGGER
          20  ;   INPUT TO THE COUNTER
          21  ;


TOTAL ERRORS:          0


SYMBOL           VALUE      LINE #
_____
CNTR1             31          5
CONP              33          6    ◄───────── SYMBOL TABLE
```

Figure 9.2: *A complete listing of an assembled program. The symbol table is given at the end of the assembly.*

device, usually the microprocessor, when developing a program for a microprocessor-controlled system. Using this approach, it is possible to suspend the program, modify it, and keep it in RAM memory. A disadvantage of a simulator is that its execution speed is slower than a normal microprocessor. Therefore, it is not possible to test "real time" devices. These are devices whose operation depends on the microprocessor system operating at normal speed.

An emulator is essentially a simulator in real time. An emulator uses one processor to simulate another one.

Utility routines are general-purpose routines which every user has access to. Examples of these routines can be examining memory data or interpreting a keyboard input. These routines are not difficult to write, but since users normally will make use of them, the manufacturer provides them. Figure 9.3 shows a memory map for a typical development system.

THE SOFTWARE DEVELOPMENT SEQUENCE

We will now examine a typical sequence for developing an assembly-level program. We will assume that all the usual software facilities are available so that we may demonstrate their value. If they are not available

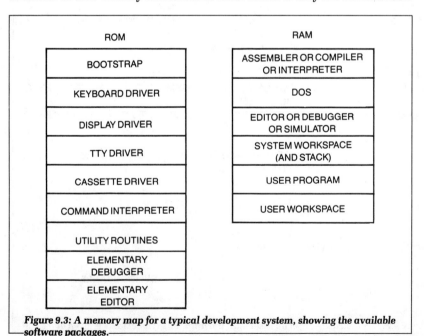

Figure 9.3: A memory map for a typical development system, showing the available software packages.

in a particular system, we can still develop programs, but the convenience will be decreased. Also the amount of time to do the development will likely increase.

Recall that the normal approach for developing an assembly-level program is to design an algorithm for the problem to be solved. Next, it is important to develop a comprehensive set of flowcharts that represent the program flow. Finally, the flowcharts are translated into an assembly-level language for the microprocessor. Once the program has been written, the next step is to enter it into a computer. A program can be entered in the RAM memory of the system under the control of the editor.

Prior to testing the program, the assembler must translate it into binary code. If the assembler does not already reside in the system, the programmer must load it from an external storage device, such as a disk.

The assembly process provides an object program that is ready to be executed. After the assembly process, instructions are in machine code or object code. The machine or microprocessor can execute this type of code directly.

Next, to verify the operation of a program, the debugger can be used to set a number of breakpoints at crucial locations in order to test intermediate results.

An *in-circuit emulator* can be used to test the program. This emulator is equipped with a cable that is terminated by a 40-pin connector identical to the pinout of the 8086/8088. If we insert this connector on the application board we are developing, the signals generated by the emulator will be exactly like those of the 8086/8088, only perhaps a little slower.

The advantage of using an in-circuit emulator is that the program can continue to reside in RAM (random access memory), thus making it easier to make changes than if the program were in the EPROM (a type of ROM). Further, the emulator can communicate with all I/O devices of the development board. This advantage, and the fact that all of the system debugging resources are available, makes the in-circuit emulator an extremely attractive tool in program development.

This completes our description of the usual sequence of events involved in developing a program. We will now review the hardware alternatives for developing programs.

HARDWARE ALTERNATIVES

There are many different hardware systems available for program development, and these systems vary in cost and capabilities. Usually the more expensive the system, the more tools it provides for developing programs.

SINGLE-BOARD MICROCOMPUTER

A single-board microcomputer offers the lowest cost approach to program development. It is normally equipped with a hexadecimal keyboard, plus some function keys and LEDs, which display information. On most single-board microcomputers there is no assembler available. Single-board microcomputers have a small monitor with limited debugging and editing facilities. Based on these limitations, programs are entered in hexadecimal form, and displayed in hexadecimal form on the system LEDs.

A single-board microcomputer has, in theory, the same hardware and power as any other computer. However, because of its restricted memory size and keyboard, it can not support the usual facilities of a larger system. This makes program development a much slower process. Due to the program development limitations of a single-board microcomputer, this type of microcomputer is best-suited for use as a training and educational tool. Single-board computers are probably the least expensive way to learn programming through actual practice.

THE DEVELOPMENT SYSTEM

A *development* system is a microcomputer system specifically designed to make the development of programs an easier task. It is usually equipped with the following items:

1. a RAM memory (a large amount)

2. a CRT display

3. a printer

4. a disk I/O

5. a PROM programmer

6. an in-circuit emulator (sometimes)

A development system normally offers all or most of the software capabilities listed in the previous section. In the best case, it is the ideal software development tool.

HOBBY-TYPE MICROCOMPUTERS

The hobby-type microcomputer hardware is similar to that of a development system. However, its software capabilities are not as sophisticated as those of an industrial-type development system. Such a system is like the one described in the previous section. As an example, most hobby-type microcomputers offer only elementary assemblers, and minimal editors and file systems. These systems represent an intermediate step between the single-board microcomputer and the full microprocessor development system. For a user who wishes to develop programs of modest complexity, these systems are probably the best compromise. Even with their limitations, they still offer the advantages of low cost, and a reasonable array of software development tools.

SUMMARY OF HARDWARE RESOURCES

We can distinguish three broad catagories of hardware systems:

1. single-board microcomputers

2. full development systems

3. hobby-type microcomputers

The single-board microcomputer is available for those who have a minimal budget and want to learn how to program. You can use this type of system to develop all the programs given in this text, as well as many others. If it is ever necessary to develop programs longer than a few hundred lines, you may find the single-board microcomputer to be inadequate.

A full development system is available for the industrial user. Any solution short of a full-development system will cause an increase in program development time. The trade-off is clear: hardware resources versus programming time. Naturally, if the programs being developed are simple, there are less expensive approaches; but if the programs are complex, it is difficult to justify any hardware savings, since the programming costs are generally the dominant cost of a project.

A hobby-type microcomputer development system offers sufficient, although minimal, facilities. This is changing, however. Very good software development tools are becoming available for personal computer systems.

THE ASSEMBLER

Let us now examine in more detail one very useful development tool: the assembler. An assembler allows the convenient symbolic representation of a user program. From this symbolic or mnemonic representation, the assembler produces a binary or object form of the instructions.

ASSEMBLER FIELDS

When typing in a program for the assembler, three fields are used:

1. **Label Field**   *(This field is optional, and may contain a symbolic address for the instruction that follows.)*

2. **Instruction Field**   *(This field includes the opcode and any operands.)*

3. **Comment Field**   *(This field is optional and intended to make the program easier to read and understand.)*

Figure 9.4 presents a diagram showing these fields.

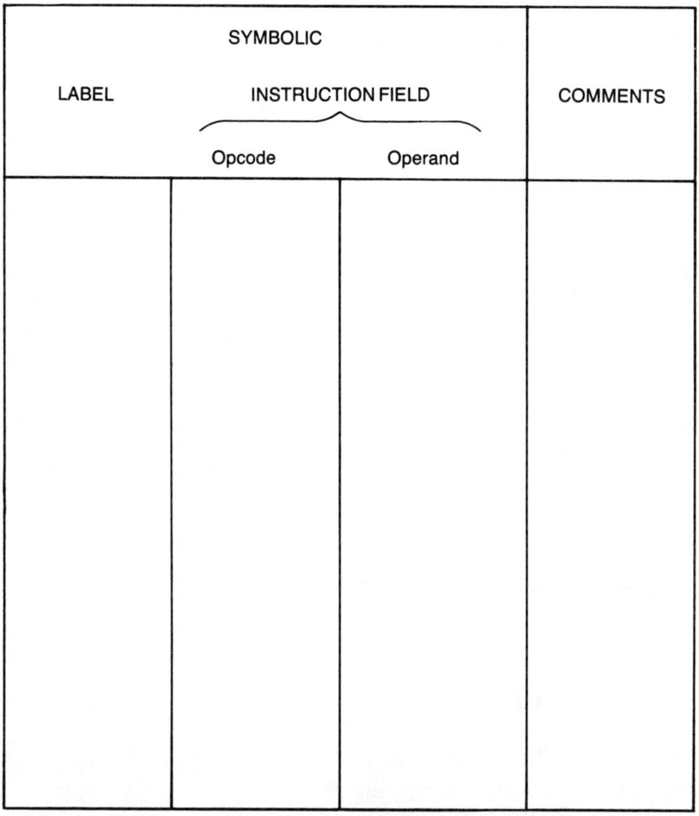

LABEL	SYMBOLIC INSTRUCTION FIELD		COMMENTS
	Opcode	Operand	

Figure 9.4: The assembler fields from left to right are label, instruction, and comment.

Once a program is input to the assembler, a listing is produced. As the listing is generated, three new fields are added on to the extreme left column of the paper or display. These new fields are the memory address, the bytes of the object code, and the line number. Figure 9.5 shows an example of an assembler output that show these new fields.

TABLES

When the assembler translates the mnemonics into the object code, it also translates the symbols used for addresses and constants into their binary equivalent. To help in program debugging, the assembler shows

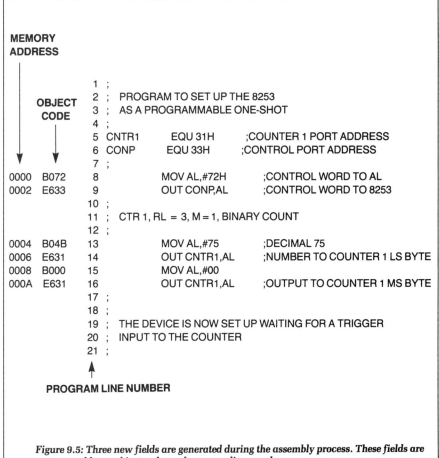

Figure 9.5: Three new fields are generated during the assembly process. These fields are memory address, object code, and program line number.

each symbol, and it shows where it is referenced in the program. This is called the *symbol table*. Figure 9.6 shows an example of a symbol table.

ERROR MESSAGES

During the assembly process, the assembler may detect syntax errors. It will include them as part of the final listing. Typical diagnostics include: undefined symbols, label already defined, illegal opcode, illegal address, and illegal addressing mode. Many additional diagnostics are desirable and are usually provided. Such features will vary with each assembler. Figure 9.7 shows a listing with error messages generated by the assembler.

SYMBOL	VALUE	LINE #
ACCUM	2C1D	1611
ADDREG	F4	36
ALPHA	30D	535
ALPHA1	317	540
ALPHA2	31E	544
AX__REG	2C31	1615
BI	20	39
BLKRAT	3E8	24
BO	10	40
BOOT	7D2	1423
BOOT1	7D5	1424
BP__REG	2C3B	1620
BREAK	6D4	1299
BRKDAT	2C2B	1613
BRKFLG	2C30	1614
BS	8	16
BUFEND	2C8D	1630
BUFFER	2C4D	1629
BUMP	305	517
BUMP0	304	516
BX__REG	2C37	1618
CAPKEY	6	262
CAPS	2C0D	1606
CHAR	2C10	1609
CLRLIN	23F	370
CLRLN1	24B	375
CMDREG	F3	35

Figure 9.6: An example of a symbol table generated by the assembler.

THE ASSEMBLY LANGUAGE

We have previously discussed opcodes. We will now define the symbols, constants, and operators that can be used as part of the assembler syntax.

SYMBOLS

Symbols are used to represent numerical values, either data or addresses. Symbols may vary in their legal length. Usually a symbol starts with an alphabetic character. Symbols may not appear the same as the mnemonics used for the 8086/8088. For example, you may not choose a symbol that is labeled DX, as this would cause confusion between the symbol and the DX register of the CPU. Documentation for an assembler gives valid descriptions for symbols.

There is a special assembler directive, EQU or equate, that can be used to assign a value to a symbol. This directive serves as an instruction to the

```
            1  ;
            2  ;   PROGRAM TO SET UP THE 8253
            3  ;   AS A PROGRAMMABLE ONE-SHOT
            4  ;
            5  CNTR1      EQU 31H        ;COUNTER 1 PORT ADDRESS
            6  CONP       EQU 33H        ;CONTROL PORT ADDRESS
            7  ;
0000 A07200 8             MOV AL,72H     ;CONTROL WORD TO AL
            9             OUT CONP,BL     ;CONTROL WORD TO 8253
 * * * * *  INVALID OPERAND   * * * * *
           10  ;
           11  ;   CTR 1, RL = 3, M = 1, BINARY COUNT
           12  ;
0003 B04B  13             MOV AL,#75     ;DECIMAL 75
0005 E643  14             OUT CNTR1,AL    ;NUMBER TO COUNTER 1 LS BYTE
           15             MVI AL,#00
 * * * * *  INVALID MNEMONIC   * * * * *
           16  ;
0007 E631  17             OUT (CNTR1) + 1,AL ;OUTPUT TO COUNTER 1 MS BYTE
 * * * *  INVALID EXPRESSION   * * * *
           18  ;
           19  ;
           20  ;   THE DEVICE IS NOW SET UP WAITING FOR A TRIGGER
           21  ;   INPUT TO THE COUNTER
           22  ;
```

Figure 9.7: An assembler listing showing error messages.

assembler only and will not be translated into object code. Figure 9.8 gives an example of symbols used in programming and values assigned by the EQU statement.

LABELS

Labels are special symbols with values that do not need to be defined by the programmer. These values are automatically defined by the assembler at the time of program assembly. (A value is assigned the memory location of the line on which it appears.) Figure 9.9 shows a label that has been given a value by the assembler. When the program is assembled, the memory address of ADDR1 will be used for the MOV instruction.

Constants or Literals

Constants may be expressed in decimal, hexadecimal, octal, binary, or as alphanumeric strings. Symbols used to represent the number bases vary from assembler to assembler. Figure 9.10 shows the different ways to represent data with one 8086/8088 assembler.

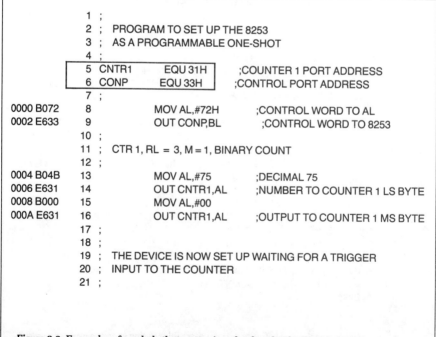

```
            1 ;
            2 ;   PROGRAM TO SET UP THE 8253
            3 ;   AS A PROGRAMMABLE ONE-SHOT
            4 ;
            5  CNTR1      EQU 31H       ;COUNTER 1 PORT ADDRESS
            6  CONP       EQU 33H       ;CONTROL PORT ADDRESS
            7 ;
0000 B072   8              MOV AL,#72H      ;CONTROL WORD TO AL
0002 E633   9              OUT CONP,BL      ;CONTROL WORD TO 8253
           10 ;
           11 ;   CTR 1, RL = 3, M = 1, BINARY COUNT
           12 ;
0004 B04B  13              MOV AL,#75       ;DECIMAL 75
0006 E631  14              OUT CNTR1,AL     ;NUMBER TO COUNTER 1 LS BYTE
0008 B000  15              MOV AL,#00
000A E631  16              OUT CNTR1,AL     ;OUTPUT TO COUNTER 1 MS BYTE
           17 ;
           18 ;
           19 ;   THE DEVICE IS NOW SET UP WAITING FOR A TRIGGER
           20 ;   INPUT TO THE COUNTER
           21 ;
```

Figure 9.8: Examples of symbols that are assigned values by the EQU statement.

OPERATORS

To make the writing of assembly language programs easier, the assembler allows the use of *operators*. At a minimum, an assembler allows the use of plus and minus; for example:

MOV AX,ADR1 + 2
MOV AX,ADR1 − 5

```
              1  ;
              2  ;    PROGRAM TO SET UP THE 8253
              3  ;    AS A PROGRAMMABLE ONE-SHOT
              4  ;
              5  CNTR1    EQU 31H          ;COUNTER 1 PORT ADDRESS
              6  CONP     EQU 33H          ;CONTROL PORT ADDRESS
              7  ;
0000  B072    8  SUB1     MOV AL,#72H      ;CONTROL WORD TO AL
0002  E633    9           OUT CONP,AL      ;CONTROL WORD TO 8253
             10  ;
             11  ;    CTR 1, RL = 3, M = 1, BINARY COUNT
             12  ;
0004  B04B   13           MOV AL,#75       ;DECIMAL 75
0006  E631   14           OUT CNTR1,AL     ;NUMBER TO COUNTER 1 LS BYTE
0008  B000   15           MOV AL,#00
000A  E631   16           OUT CNTR1,AL     ;OUTPUT TO COUNTER 1 MS BYTE
000C  A0 1000 17          MOV AL,ADDR1     ;LOAD DATA AT ADDR1 TO AL
000F  C3     18           RET              ;RETURN FROM SUB
             19  ;
             20  ;    DATA LOCATION FOLLOWS
             21  ;
0010  01     22  ADDR1    DB  01
```

Figure 9.9: *ADDR1 is used by the MOV instruction as an address.*

```
              1  ;
              2  ;   DIFFERENT WAYS TO REPRESENT DATA
              3  ;   WITH ONE 8086/8088 ASSEMBLER
              4  ;
0000 B031     5           MOV AL,#00110001P  ;BINARY NOTATION
0002 B031     6           MOV AL,#31H        ;HEXADECIMAL NOTATION
0004 B031     7           MOV AL,#49         ;DECIMAL NOTATION
0006 B031     8           MOV AL,#61Q        ;OCTAL NOTATION
              9  ;
             10  ;
```

Figure 9.10: *Assemblers allow different ways to represent data.*

It is important to understand that the expression ADR1 + 2 or ADR1 − 5 is computed by the assembler at the time of assembly. Figure 9.11 shows an example of operator use.

ASSEMBLER DIRECTIVES

Directives are special orders given by the programmer to the assembler. Directives do not get translated into object code for the microprocessor. Let us review some of the common directives for an assembler. Let's start with:

> ORG nn

This directive sets the assembler address counter to the value nn. In other words, the first executable instruction encountered after the ORG will begin at memory address nn. You can use the ORG statement at any point in the program to change the value of the assembler memory address. A second assembler directive is EQU:

> MY_ADD EQU nn

The label MY_ADD is equated to the numerical value nn at the time of assembly.

To form a single byte the directive DB (for define byte) is used, for example:

> ONE DB 01

The label ONE is assigned an 8-bit quantity, 00000001. If we wish to define

```
            1 ;
            2 ;   PROGRAM TO SHOW HOW + AND −
            3 ;   OPERATORS WORK
            4 ;
            5 ADDR1    EQU 0123H
            6 ;
0000 8B1E2301  7          MOV BX, ADDR1    ;DATA AT ADDR1 IS MOVED TO BX
0004 8B0E2501  8   MOV CX,ADDR1 + 2    ;DATA AT ADDR1 + 2 IS MOVED TO CX
            9 ;
```

Figure 9.11: *Most assemblers allow the use of expressions that are evaluated at the time of assembly.*

a label as a 16-bit quantity, we can use the directive DW (for define word). It looks like this:

TWO DW 02

The label TWO equals the 16-bit value of 0000 0000 0000 0010.

We can also define a double word (or 32 bits) by using the directive DD (for define double word). We could use it in the following way:

BIG__NUMBER DD 45860912H

The binary value of BIG__NUMBER requires four bytes of memory to completely specify its value.

If we wish to define a string constant for a message that may be printed out, we could also use the directive DB. For example, let's suppose we wish to store the message "ERROR 5 - ILLEGAL VALUE." We could include it in the program like this:

ERR5 DB 'ERROR 5 - ILLEGAL VALUE'

The assembler will set the ASCII equivalent of each character into memory. There will be 23 bytes of memory used for the storage of this message. Depending on how your system operates, there may be one extra byte used to terminate or show the end of the message. Some assemblers use different directives for this activity. Popular directive symbols are DS (for define storage) and DT (for define text).

The END directive is used to inform the assembler that there will be no more instructions to assemble. The assembler will not look for any statements, following this directive.

CHAPTER SUMMARY

In this chapter we have examined the techniques, and hardware and software tools required to develop programs. We have also discussed different trade-offs and alternatives for the tools available for program development. The techniques we have discussed have ranged from a single-board microcomputer to a full development system. We have concluded the discussion with an examination of some common points about microprocessor assembler programs.

CONCLUSION

In this book, we have covered the important aspects of programming the 8086/8088. The first chapter began with a discussion of the basic definitions and concepts of programming. We then went on to explore and discuss the specifics of the 8086/8088 CPU. Next, we examined the use of I/O devices and various software development tools.[1]

What then is the next step? After reading this book, you should now be ready to go off on your own and write your own programs on the 8086/8088. As you continue to do this, you will discover that the instruction set, for these microprocessors is very powerful. As you gain more and more experience in using the various instructions, you will discover new and creative ways to solve your application problems. This is when the real fun begins.

So good luck and productive programming!!!

---

[1] There is an 8086/8088 microprocessor trainer available from Creative Microprocessor Systems (P.O. Box 1538, Los Gatos, CA 95030). This trainer employs a single-line assembler that allows you to program in assembly language. It is a unique and valuable tool for gaining experience in programming the 8086/8088.

APPENDIX A
HEXADECIMAL
CONVERSION TABLE

HEX	0	1	2	3	4	5	6	7	8	9	A	B	C	D	E	F	00	000
0	0	1	2	3	4	5	6	7	8	9	10	11	12	13	14	15	0	0
1	16	17	18	19	20	21	22	23	24	25	26	27	28	29	30	31	256	4096
2	32	33	34	35	36	37	38	39	40	41	42	43	44	45	46	47	512	8192
3	48	49	50	51	52	53	54	55	56	57	58	59	60	61	62	63	768	12288
4	64	65	66	67	68	69	70	71	72	73	74	75	76	77	78	79	1024	16384
5	80	81	82	83	84	85	86	87	88	89	90	91	92	93	94	95	1280	20480
6	96	97	98	99	100	101	102	103	104	105	106	107	108	109	110	111	1536	24576
7	112	113	114	115	116	117	118	119	120	121	122	123	124	125	126	127	1792	28672
8	128	129	130	131	132	133	134	135	136	137	138	139	140	141	142	143	2048	32768
9	144	145	146	147	148	149	150	151	152	153	154	155	156	157	158	159	2304	36864
A	160	161	162	163	164	165	166	167	168	169	170	171	172	173	174	175	2560	40960
B	176	177	178	179	180	181	182	183	184	185	186	187	188	189	190	191	2816	45056
C	192	193	194	195	196	197	198	199	200	201	202	203	204	205	206	207	3072	49152
D	208	209	210	211	212	213	214	215	216	217	218	219	220	221	222	223	3328	53248
E	224	225	226	227	228	229	230	231	232	233	234	235	236	237	238	239	3584	57344
F	240	241	242	243	244	245	246	247	248	249	250	251	252	253	254	255	3840	61440

5		4		3		2		1		0	
HEX	DEC	HEX	DEC	HEX	DEC	HEX	DEC	HEX	DEC	HEX	DEC
0	0	0	0	0	0	0	0	0	0	0	0
1	1,048,576	1	65,536	1	4,096	1	256	1	16	1	1
2	2,097,152	2	131,072	2	8,192	2	512	2	32	2	2
3	3,145,728	3	196,608	3	12,288	3	768	3	48	3	3
4	4,194,304	4	262,144	4	16,384	4	1,024	4	64	4	4
5	5,242,880	5	327,680	5	20,480	5	1,280	5	80	5	5
6	6,291,456	6	393,216	6	24,576	6	1,536	6	96	6	6
7	7,340,032	7	458,752	7	28,672	7	1,792	7	112	7	7
8	8,388,608	8	524,288	8	32,768	8	2,048	8	128	8	8
9	9,437,184	9	589,824	9	36,864	9	2,304	9	144	9	9
A	10,485,760	A	655,360	A	40,960	A	2,560	A	160	A	10
B	11,534,336	B	720,896	B	45,056	B	2,816	B	176	B	11
C	12,582,912	C	786,432	C	49,152	C	3,072	C	192	C	12
D	13,631,488	D	851,968	D	53,248	D	3,328	D	208	D	13
E	14,680,064	E	917,504	E	57,344	E	3,584	E	224	E	14
F	15,728,640	F	983,040	F	61,440	F	3,840	F	240	F	15

APPENDIX B
ASCII CONVERSION TABLE

HEX LSD	MSD BITS	0 000	1 001	2 010	3 011	4 100	5 101	6 110	7 111
0	0000	NUL	DLE	SPACE	0	@	P	—	p
1	0001	SOH	DC1	!	1	A	Q	a	q
2	0010	STX	DC2	''	2	B	R	b	r
3	0011	ETX	DC3	#	3	C	S	c	s
4	0100	EOT	DC4	$	4	D	T	d	t
5	0101	ENQ	NAK	%	5	E	U	e	u
6	0110	ACK	SYN	&	6	F	V	f	v
7	0111	BEL	ETB	'	7	G	W	g	w
8	1000	BS	CAN	(	8	H	X	h	x
9	1001	HT	EM	)	9	I	Y	i	y
A	1010	LF	SUB	*	:	J	Z	j	z
B	1011	VT	ESC	+	;	K	[	k	{
C	1100	FF	FS	,	<	L	\	l	--
D	1101	CR	GS	—	=	M	]	m	}
E	1110	SO	RS	.	>	N	^	n	~
F	1111	SI	US	/	?	O	←	o	DEL

THE ASCII SYMBOLS

NUL	— Null	DLE	— Data Link Escape
SOH	— Start of Heading	DC	— Device Control
STX	— Start of Text	NAK	— Negative Acknowledge
ETX	— End of Text	SYN	— Synchronous Idle
EOT	— End of Transmission	ETB	— End of Transmission Block
ENQ	— Enquiry	CAN	— Cancel
ACK	— Acknowledge	EM	— End of Medium
BEL	— Bell	SUB	— Substitute
BS	— Backspace	ESC	— Escape
HT	— Horizontal Tabulation	FS	— File Separator
LF	— Line Feed	GS	— Group Separator
VT	— Vertical Tabulation	RS	— Record Separator
FF	— Form Feed	US	— Unit Separator
CR	— Carriage Return	SP	— Space (Blank)
SO	— Shift Out	DEL	— Delete
SI	— Shift In		

APPENDIX C
DECIMAL TO BCD
CONVERSION TABLE

DECIMAL	BCD	DEC	BCD	DEC	BCD
0	0000	10	00010000	91	10010000
1	0001	11	00010001	91	10010001
2	0010	12	00010010	92	10010010
3	0011	13	00010011	93	10010011
4	0100	14	00010100	94	10010100
5	0101	15	00010101	95	10010101
6	0110	16	00010110	96	10010110
7	0111	17	00010111	97	10010111
8	1000	18	00011000	98	10011000
9	1001	19	00011001	99	10011001

APPENDIX D 8086/8088 INSTRUCTION SET REFERENCE DATA

AAA	AAA (no operands) ASCII adjust for addition				Flags	O D I T S Z A P C U U U X U X
Operands	Clocks	Transfers*	Bytes		**Coding Example**	
(no operands)	4	—	1		AAA	

AAD	AAD (no operands) ASCII adjust for division				Flags	O D I T S Z A P C U X X U X U
Operands	Clocks	Transfers*	Bytes		**Coding Example**	
(no operands)	60	—	2		AAD	

AAM	AAM (no operands) ASCII adjust for multiply				Flags	O D I T S Z A P C U X X U X U
Operands	Clocks	Transfers*	Bytes		**Coding Example**	
(no operands)	83	—	1		AAM	

AAS	AAS (no operands) ASCII adjust for subtraction				Flags	O D I T S Z A P C U U U X U X
Operands	Clocks	Transfers*	Bytes		**Coding Example**	
(no operands)	4	—	1		AAS	

ADC	ADC destination,source Add with carry				Flags	O D I T S Z A P C X X X X X X
Operands	Clocks	Transfers*	Bytes		**Coding Example**	
register, register	3	—	2		ADC AX, SI	
register, memory	9 + EA	1	2-4		ADC DX, BETA [SI]	
memory, register	16 + EA	2	2-4		ADC ALPHA [BX] [SI], DI	
register, immediate	4	—	3-4		ADC BX, 256	
memory, immediate	17 + EA	2	3-6		ADC GAMMA, 30H	
accumulator, immediate	4	—	2-3		ADC AL, 5	

*For the 8086, add four clocks for each 16-bit word transfer with an odd address. For the 8088, add four clocks for each 16-bit word transfer.

Mnemonics © Intel, 1978

ADD	ADD destination,source Addition			Flags	O D I T S Z A P C X X X X X X
Operands	Clocks	Transfers*	Bytes	Coding Example	
register, register	3	—	2	ADD CX, DX	
register, memory	9 + EA	1	2-4	ADD DI, [BX].ALPHA	
memory, register	16 + EA	2	2-4	ADD TEMP, CL	
register, immediate	4	—	3-4	ADD CL, 2	
memory, immediate	17 + EA	2	3-6	ADD ALPHA, 2	
accumulator, immediate	4	—	2-3	ADD AX, 200	

AND	AND destination,source Logical and			Flags	O D I T S Z A P C 0 X X U X 0
Operands	Clocks	Transfers*	Bytes	Coding Example	
register, register	3	—	2	AND AL,BL	
register, memory	9 + EA	1	2-4	AND CX,FLAG__WORD	
memory, register	16 + EA	2	2-4	AND ASCII [DI],AL	
register, immediate	4	—	3-4	AND CX,0F0H	
memory, immediate	17 + EA	2	3-6	AND BETA, 01H	
accumulator, immediate	4	—	2-3	AND AX, 01010000B	

CALL	CALL target Call a procedure			Flags	O D I T S Z A P C
Operands	Clocks	Transfers*	Bytes	Coding Examples	
near-proc	19	1	3	CALL NEAR__PROC	
far-proc	28	2	5	CALL FAR__PROC	
memptr 16	21 + EA	2	2-4	CALL PROC__TABLE [SI]	
regptr 16	16	1	2	CALL AX	
memptr 32	37 + EA	4	2-4	CALL [BX].TASK [SI]	

CBW	CBW (no operands) Convert byte to word			Flags	O D I T S Z A P C
Operands	Clocks	Transfers*	Bytes	Coding Example	
(no operands)	2	—	1	CBW	

CLC	CLC (no operands) Clear carry flag			Flags	O D I T S Z A P C 0
Operands	Clocks	Transfers*	Bytes	Coding Example	
(no operands)	2	—	1	CLC	

CLD	CLD (no operands) Clear direction flag			Flags	O D I T S Z A P C 0
Operands	Clocks	Transfers*	Bytes	Coding Example	
(no operands)	2	—	1	CLD	

*For the 8086, add four clocks for each 16-bit word transfer with an odd address. For the 8088, add four clocks for each 16-bit word transfer.

Mnemonics © Intel, 1978

CLI	CLI (no operands) Clear interrupt flag			Flags	O D I T S Z A P C 0
Operands	**Clocks**	**Transfers***	**Bytes**	**Coding Example**	
(no operands)	2	—	1	CLI	

CMC	CMC (no operands) Complement carry flag			Flags	O D I T S Z A P C X
Operands	**Clocks**	**Transfers***	**Bytes**	**Coding Example**	
(no operands)	2	—	1	CMC	

CMP	CMP destination,source Compare destination to source			Flags	O D I T S Z A P C X X X X X X
Operands	**Clocks**	**Transfers***	**Bytes**	**Coding Example**	
register, register	3	—	2	CMP BX, CX	
register, memory	9 + EA	1	2-4	CMP DH, ALPHA	
memory, register	9 + EA	1	2-4	CMP [BP + 2], SI	
register, immediate	4	—	3-4	CMP BL, 02H	
memory, immediate	10 + EA	1	3-6	CMP [BX].RADAR [DI], 3420H	
accumulator, immediate	4	—	2-3	CMP AL. 00010000B	

CMPS	CMPS dest-string,source-string Compare string			Flags	O D I T S Z A P C X X X X X X
Operands	**Clocks**	**Transfers***	**Bytes**	**Coding Example**	
dest-string, source-string	22	2	1	CMPS BUFF1, BUFF2	
(repeat) dest-string, source-string	9 + 22/rep	2/rep	1	REPE CMPS ID. KEY	

CWD	CWD (no operands) Convert word to doubleword			Flags	O D I T S Z A P C
Operands	**Clocks**	**Transfers***	**Bytes**	**Coding Example**	
(no operands)	5	—	1	CWD	

DAA	DAA (no operands) Decimal adjust for addition			Flags	O D I T S Z A P C X X X X X X
Operands	**Clocks**	**Transfers***	**Bytes**	**Coding Example**	
(no operands)	4	—	1	DAA	

DAS	DAS (no operands) Decimal adjust for subtraction			Flags	O D I T S Z A P C U X X X X X
Operands	**Clocks**	**Transfers***	**Bytes**	**Coding Example**	
(no operands)	4	—	1	DAS	

*For the 8086, add four clocks for each 16-bit word transfer with an odd address. For the 8088, add four clocks for each 16-bit word transfer.
Mnemonics © Intel, 1978

DEC	**DEC** destination Decrement by 1			Flags	O D I T S Z A P C X X X X X
Operands	Clocks	Transfers*	Bytes	Coding Example	
reg16	2	—	1	DEC AX	
reg8	3	—	2	DEC AL	
memory	15 + EA	2	2-4	DEC ARRAY [SI]	

DIV	**DIV** source Division, unsigned			Flags	O D I T S Z A P C U U U U U
Operands	Clocks	Transfers*	Bytes	Coding Example	
reg8	80-90	—	2	DIV CL	
reg16	144-162	—	2	DIV BX	
mem8	(86-96) + EA	1	2-4	DIV ALPHA	
mem16	(150-168) + EA	1	2-4	DIV TABLE [SI]	

ESC	**ESC** external-opcode,source Escape			Flags	O D I T S Z A P C
Operands	Clocks	Transfers*	Bytes	Coding Example	
immediate, memory	8 + EA	1	2-4	ESC 6,ARRAY [SI]	
immediate, register	2	—	2	ESC 20,AL	

HLT	**HLT** (no operands) Halt			Flags	O D I T S Z A P C
Operands	Clocks	Transfers*	Bytes	Coding Example	
(no operands)	2	—	1	HLT	

IDIV	**IDIV** source Integer division			Flags	O D I T S Z A P C U U U U U
Operands	Clocks	Transfers*	Bytes	Coding Example	
reg8	101-112	—	2	IDIV BL	
reg16	165-184	—	2	IDIV CX	
mem8	(107-118) + EA	1	2-4	IDIV DIVISOR__BYTE [SI]	
mem16	(171-190) + EA	1	2-4	IDIV [BX].DIVISOR__WORD	

*For the 8086, add four clocks for each 16-bit word transfer with an odd address. For the 8088, add four clocks for each 16-bit word transfer.
Mnemonics © Intel, 1978

IMUL	IMUL source Integer multiplication			Flags	O D I T S Z A P C X U U U U X
Operands	Clocks	Transfers*	Bytes	Coding Example	
reg8	80-98	—	2	IMUL CL	
reg16	128-154	—	2	IMUL BX	
mem8	(86-104) + EA	1	2-4	IMUL RATE BYTE	
mem16	(134-160) + EA	1	2-4	IMUL RATE WORD [BP] [DI]	

IN	IN accumulator,port Input byte or word			Flags	O D I T S Z A P C
Operands	Clocks	Transfers*	Bytes	Coding Example	
accumulator, immed8	10	1	2	IN AL. 0FFEAH	
accumulator, DX	8	1	1	IN AX. DX	

INC	INC destination Increment by 1			Flags	O D I T S Z A P C X X X X X
Operands	Clocks	Transfers*	Bytes	Coding Example	
reg16	2	—	1	INC CX	
reg8	3	—	2	INC BL	
memory	15 + EA	2	2-4	INC ALPHA [DI] [BX]	

INT	INT interrupt-type Interrupt			Flags	O D I T S Z A P C 0 0
Operands	Clocks	Transfers*	Bytes	Coding Example	
immed8 (type = 3)	52	5	1	INT 3	
immed8 (type ≠ 3)	51	5	2	INT 67	

INTR†	INTR (external maskable interrupt) Interrupt if INTR and IF=1			Flags	O D I T S Z A P C 0 0
Operands	Clocks	Transfers*	Bytes	Coding Example	
(no operands)	61	7	N/A	N/A	

INTO	INTO (no operands) Interrupt if overflow			Flags	O D I T S Z A P C 0 0
Operands	Clocks	Transfers*	Bytes	Coding Example	
(no operands)	53 or 4	5	1	INTO	

*For the 8086, add four clocks for each 16-bit word transfer with an odd address. For the 8088, add four clocks for each 16-bit word transfer.

†INTR is not an instruction; it is included only for timing information.

Mnemonics © Intel, 1978

IRET	IRET (no operands) Interrupt Return			Flags	O D I T S Z A P C R R R R R R R R
Operands	Clocks	Transfers*	Bytes	Coding Example	
(no operands)	24	3	1	IRET	

JA/JNBE	JA/JNBE short-label Jump if above/Jump if not below nor equal			Flags	O D I T S Z A P C
Operands	Clocks	Transfers*	Bytes	Coding Example	
short-label	16 or 4	—	2	JA ABOVE	

JAE/JNB	JAE/JNB short-label Jump if above or equal/Jump if not below			Flags	O D I T S Z A P C
Operands	Clocks	Transfers*	Bytes	Coding Example	
short-label	16 or 4	—	2	JAE ABOVE EQUAL	

JB/JNAE	JB/JNAE short-label Jump if below/Jump if not above nor equal			Flags	O D I T S Z A P C
Operands	Clocks	Transfers*	Bytes	Coding Example	
short-label	16 or 4	—	2	JB BELOW	

JBE/JNA	JBE/JNA short-label Jump if below or equal/Jump if not above			Flags	O D I T S Z A P C
Operands	Clocks	Transfers*	Bytes	Coding Example	
short-label	16 or 4	—	2	JNA NOT ABOVE	

JC	JC short-label Jump if carry			Flags	O D I T S Z A P C
Operands	Clocks	Transfers*	Bytes	Coding Example	
short-label	16 or 4	—	2	JC CARRY SET	

JCXZ	JCXZ short-label Jump if CX is zero			Flags	O D I T S Z A P C
Operands	Clocks	Transfers*	Bytes	Coding Example	
short-label	18 or 6	—	2	JCXZ COUNT DONE	

JE/JZ	JE/JZ short-label Jump if equal/Jump if zero			Flags	O D I T S Z A P C
Operands	Clocks	Transfers*	Bytes	Coding Example	
short-label	16 or 4	—	2	JZ ZERO	

*For the 8086, add four clocks for each 16-bit word transfer with an odd address. For the 8088, add four clocks for each 16-bit word transfer.

Mnemonics © Intel, 1978

JG/JNLE	JG/JNLE short-label Jump if greater/Jump if not less nor equal			Flags	O D I T S Z A P C
Operands	**Clocks**	**Transfers***	**Bytes**	**Coding Example**	
short-label	16 or 4	—	2	JG GREATER	

JGE/JNL	JGE/JNL short-label Jump if greater or equal/Jump if not less			Flags	O D I T S Z A P C
Operands	**Clocks**	**Transfers***	**Bytes**	**Coding Example**	
short-label	16 or 4	—	2	JGE GREATER_EQUAL	

JL/JNGE	JL/JNGE short-label Jump if less/Jump if not greater nor equal			Flags	O D I T S Z A P C
Operands	**Clocks**	**Transfers***	**Bytes**	**Coding Example**	
short-label	16 or 4	—	2	JL LESS	

JLE/JNG	JLE/JNG short-label Jump if less or equal/Jump if not greater			Flags	O D I T S Z A P C
Operands	**Clocks**	**Transfers***	**Bytes**	**Coding Example**	
short-label	16 or 4	—	2	JNG NOT_GREATER	

JMP	JMP target Jump			Flags	O D I T S Z A P C
Operands	**Clocks**	**Transfers***	**Bytes**	**Coding Example**	
short-label	15	—	2	JMP SHORT	
near-label	15	—	3	JMP WITHIN_SEGMENT	
far-label	15	—	5	JMP FAR_LABEL	
memptr16	18 + EA	1	2-4	JMP [BX].TARGET	
regptr16	11	—	2	JMP CX	
memptr32	24 + EA	2	2-4	JMP OTHER.SEG [SI]	

JNC	JNC short-label Jump if not carry			Flags	O D I T S Z A P C
Operands	**Clocks**	**Transfers***	**Bytes**	**Coding Example**	
short-label	16 or 4	—	2	JNC NOT_CARRY	

JNE/JNZ	JNE/JNZ short-label Jump if not equal/Jump if not zero			Flags	O D I T S Z A P C
Operands	**Clocks**	**Transfers***	**Bytes**	**Coding Example**	
short-label	16 or 4	—	2	JNE NOT_EQUAL	

*For the 8086, add four clocks for each 16-bit word transfer with an odd address. For the 8088, add four clocks for each 16-bit word transfer.
Mnemonics © Intel, 1978

JNO	**JNO** short-label Jump if not overflow			Flags	O D I T S Z A P C
Operands	Clocks	Transfers*	Bytes		Coding Example
short-label	16 or 4	—	2		JNO NO__OVERFLOW

JNP/JPO	**JNP/JPO** short-label Jump if not parity/Jump if parity odd			Flags	O D I T S Z A P C
Operands	Clocks	Transfers*	Bytes		Coding Example
short-label	16 or 4	—	2		JPO ODD__PARITY

JNS	**JNS** short-label Jump if not sign			Flags	O D I T S Z A P C
Operands	Clocks	Transfers*	Bytes		Coding Example
short-label	16 or 4	—	2		JNS POSITIVE

JO	**JO** short-label Jump if overflow			Flags	O D I T S Z A P C
Operands	Clocks	Transfers*	Bytes		Coding Example
short-label	16 or 4	—	2		JO SIGNED__OVRFLW

JP/JPE	**JP/JPE** short-label Jump if parity/Jump if parity even			Flags	O D I T S Z A P C
Operands	Clocks	Transfers*	Bytes		Coding Example
short-label	16 or 4	—	2		JPE EVEN__PARITY

JS	**JS** short-label Jump if sign			Flags	O D I T S Z A P C
Operands	Clocks	Transfers*	Bytes		Coding Example
short-label	16 or 4	—	2		JS NEGATIVE

LAHF	**LAHF** (no operands) Load AH from flags			Flags	O D I T S Z A P C
Operands	Clocks	Transfers*	Bytes		Coding Example
(no operands)	4	—	1		LAHF

LDS	**LDS** destination,source Load pointer using DS			Flags	O D I T S Z A P C
Operands	Clocks	Transfers	Bytes		Coding Example
reg16, mem32	16 + EA	2	2-4		LDS SI,DATA.SEG [DI]

*For the 8086, add four clocks for each 16-bit word transfer with an odd address. For the 8088, add four clocks for each 16-bit word transfer.
Mnemonics © Intel, 1978

LEA	LEA destination,source Load effective address			**Flags** O D I T S Z A P C
Operands	**Clocks**	**Transfers***	**Bytes**	**Coding Example**
reg16, mem16	2 + EA	—	2-4	LEA BX, [BP] [DI]

LES	LES destination,source Load pointer using ES			**Flags** O D I T S Z A P C
Operands	**Clocks**	**Transfers***	**Bytes**	**Coding Example**
reg16, mem32	16 + EA	2	2-4	LES DI, [BX].TEXT__BUFF

LOCK	LOCK (no operands) Lock bus			**Flags** O D I T S Z A P C
Operands	**Clocks**	**Transfers***	**Bytes**	**Coding Example**
(no operands)	2	—	1	LOCK XCHG FLAG,AL

LODS	LODS source-string Load string			**Flags** O D I T S Z A P C
Operands	**Clocks**	**Transfers***	**Bytes**	**Coding Example**
source-string (repeat) source-string	12 9 + 13/rep	1 1/rep	1 1	LODS CUSTOMER__NAME REP LODS NAME

LOOP	LOOP short-label Loop			**Flags** O D I T S Z A P C
Operands	**Clocks**	**Transfers***	**Bytes**	**Coding Example**
short-label	17/5	—	2	LOOP AGAIN

LOOPE/LOOPZ	LOOPE/LOOPZ short-label Loop if equal/Loop if zero			**Flags** O D I T S Z A P C
Operands	**Clocks**	**Transfers***	**Bytes**	**Coding Example**
short-label	18 or 6	—	2	LOOPE AGAIN

LOOPNE/LOOPNZ	LOOPNE/LOOPNZ short-label Loop if not equal/Loop if not zero			**Flags** O D I T S Z A P C
Operands	**Clocks**	**Transfers***	**Bytes**	**Coding Example**
short-label	19 or 5	—	2	LOOPNE AGAIN

NMI[†]	NMI (external nonmaskable interrupt) Interrupt if NMI = 1			**Flags** O S I T S Z A P C 0 0
Operands	**Clocks**	**Transfers***	**Bytes**	**Coding Example**
(no operands)	50	5	N/A	N/A

*For the 8086, add four clocks for each 16-bit word transfer with an odd address. For the 8088, add four clocks for each 16-bit word transfer.
†NMI is not an instruction; it is included only for timing information.
Mnemonics © Intel, 1978

MOV	MOV destination,source Move				Flags	O D I T S Z A P C
Operands		**Clocks**	**Transfers***	**Bytes**	**Coding Example**	
memory, accumulator		10	1	3	MOV ARRAY [SI], AL	
accumulator, memory		10	1	3	MOV AX, TEMP__RESULT	
register, register		2	—	2	MOV AX,CX	
register, memory		8 + EA	1	2-4	MOV BP, STACK__TOP	
memory, register		9 + EA	1	2-4	MOV COUNT [DI], CX	
register, immediate		4	—	2-3	MOV CL, 2	
memory, immediate		10 + EA	1	3-6	MOV MASK [BX] [SI], 2CH	
seg-reg, reg16		2	—	2	MOV ES, CX	
seg-reg, mem16		8 + EA	1	2-4	MOV DS, SEGMENT__BASE	
reg16, seg-reg		2	—	2	MOV BP, SS	
memory, seg-reg		9 + EA	1	2-4	MOV [BX].SEG__SAVE, CS	

MOVS	MOVS dest-string,source-string Move string				Flags	O D I T S Z A P C
Operands		**Clocks**	**Transfers***	**Bytes**	**Coding Example**	
dest-string, source-string		18	2	1	MOVS LINE EDIT__DATA	
(repeat) dest-string, source-string		9 + 17/rep	2/rep	1	REP MOVS SCREEN, BUFFER	

MOVSB/MOVSW	MOVSB/MOVSW (no operands) Move string (byte/word)				Flags	O D I T S Z A P C
Operands		**Clocks**	**Transfers***	**Bytes**	**Coding Example**	
(no operands)		18	2	1	MOVSB	
(repeat) (no operands)		9 + 17/rep	2/rep	1	REP MOVSW	

MUL	MUL source Multiplication, unsigned				Flags	O D I T S Z A P C X U U U U X
Operands		**Clocks**	**Transfers***	**Bytes**	**Coding Example**	
reg8		70-77	—	2	MUL BL	
reg16		118-133	—	2	MUL CX	
mem8		(76-83) + EA	1	2-4	MUL MONTH [SI]	
mem16		(124-139) + EA	1	2-4	MUL BAUD__RATE	

NEG	NEG destination Negate				Flags	O D I T S Z A P C X X X X X 1*
Operands		**Clocks**	**Transfers***	**Bytes**	**Coding Example**	
register		3	—	2	NEG AL	
memory		16 + EA	2	2-4	NEG MULTIPLIER	

*0 if destination = 0

*For the 8086, add four clocks for each 16-bit word transfer with an odd address. For the 8088, add four clocks for each 16-bit word transfer.
Mnemonics © Intel, 1978

NOP	NOP (no operands) No Operation			Flags	O D I T S Z A P C
Operands	**Clocks**	**Transfers***	**Bytes**	**Coding Example**	
(no operands)	3	—	1	NOP	

NOT	NOT destination Logical not			Flags	O D I T S Z A P C
Operands	**Clocks**	**Transfers***	**Bytes**	**Coding Example**	
register	3	—	2	NOT AX	
memory	16 + EA	2	2-4	NOT CHARACTER	

OR	OR destination, source Logical inclusive or			Flags	O D I T S Z A P C 0 X X U X 0
Operands	**Clocks**	**Transfers***	**Bytes**	**Coding Example**	
register, register	3	—	2	OR AL, BL	
register, memory	9 + EA	1	2-4	OR DX, PORT _ID [DI]	
memory, register	16 + EA	2	2-4	OR FLAG _BYTE, CL	
accumulator, immediate	4	—	2-3	OR AL, 01101100B	
register, immediate	4	—	3-4	OR CX, 01H	
memory, immediate	17 + EA	2	3-6	OR [BX].CMD _WORD, 0CFH	

OUT	OUT port, accumulator Output byte or word			Flags	O D I T S Z A P C
Operands	**Clocks**	**Transfers***	**Bytes**	**Coding Example**	
immed8, accumulator	10	1	2	OUT 44, AX	
DX, accumulator	8	1	1	OUT DX, AL	

POP	POP destination Pop word off stack			Flags	O D I T S Z A P C
Operands	**Clocks**	**Transfers***	**Bytes**	**Coding Example**	
register	8	1	1	POP DX	
seg-reg (CS illegal)	8	1	1	POP DS	
memory	17 + EA	2	2-4	POP PARAMETER	

POPF	POPF (no operands) Pop flags off stack			Flags	O D I T S Z A P C R R R R R R R R
Operands	**Clocks**	**Transfers***	**Bytes**	**Coding Example**	
(no operands)	8	1	1	POPF	

*For the 8086, add four clocks for each 16-bit word transfer with an odd address. For the 8088, add four clocks for each 16-bit word transfer.
Mnemonics © Intel, 1978

PUSH	PUSH source Push word onto stack			Flags	O D I T S Z A P C
Operands	Clocks	Transfers*	Bytes	Coding Example	
register seg-reg (CS legal) memory	11 10 16 + EA	1 1 2	1 1 2-4	PUSH SI PUSH ES PUSH RETURN__CODE [SI]	

PUSHF	PUSHF (no operands) Push flags onto stack			Flags	O D I T S Z A P C
Operands	Clocks	Transfers*	Bytes	Coding Example	
(no operands)	10	1	1	PUSHF	

RCL	RCL destination,count Rotate left through carry			Flags	O D I T S Z A P C X X
Operands	Clocks	Transfers*	Bytes	Coding Example	
register, 1 register, CL memory, 1 memory, CL	2 8 + 4/bit 15 + EA 20 + EA + 4/bit	— — 2 2	2 2 2-4 2-4	RCL CX, 1 RCL AL, CL RCL ALPHA, 1 RCL [BP].PARM, CL	

RCR	RCR designation,count Rotate right through carry			Flags	O D I T S Z A P C X X
Operands	Clocks	Transfers*	Bytes	Coding Example	
register, 1 register, CL memory, 1 memory, CL	2 8 + 4/bit 15 + EA 20 + EA + 4/bit	— — 2 2	2 2 2-4 2-4	RCR BX, 1 RCR BL, CL RCR [BX].STATUS, 1 RCR ARRAY [DI], CL	

REP	REP (no operands) Repeat string operation			Flags	O D I T S Z A P C
Operands	Clocks	Transfers*	Bytes	Coding Example	
(no operands)	2	—	1	REP MOVS DEST, SRCE	

REPE/REPZ	REPE/REPZ (no operands) Repeat string operation while equal/while zero			Flags	O D I T S Z A P C
Operands	Clocks	Transfers*	Bytes	Coding Example	
(no operands)	2	—	1	REPE CMPS DATA, KEY	

*For the 8086, add four clocks for each 16-bit word transfer with an odd address. For the 8088, add four clocks for each 16-bit word transfer.

Mnemonics © Intel, 1978

REPNE/REPNZ

REPNE/REPNZ (no operands) Repeat string operation while not equal/not zero				Flags	O D I T S Z A P C

Operands	Clocks	Transfers*	Bytes	Coding Example
(no operands)	2	—	1	REPNE SCAS INPUT LINE

RET

RET optional-pop-value Return from procedure				Flags	O D I T S Z A P C

Operands	Clocks	Transfers*	Bytes	Coding Example
(intra-segment, no pop)	8	1	1	RET
(intra-segment, pop)	12	1	3	RET 4
(inter-segment, no pop)	18	2	1	RET
(inter-segment, pop)	17	2	3	RET 2

ROL

ROL destination,count Rotate left				Flags	O D I T S Z A P C X X

Operands	Clocks	Transfers	Bytes	Coding Examples
register, 1	2	—	2	ROL BX, 1
register, CL	8 + 4/bit	—	2	ROL DI, CL
memory, 1	15 + EA	2	2-4	ROL FLAG_BYTE [DI],1
memory, CL	20 + EA + 4/bit	2	2-4	ROL ALPHA , CL

ROR

ROR destination,count Rotate right				Flags	O D I T S Z A P C X X

Operand	Clocks	Transfers*	Bytes	Coding Example
register, 1	2	—	2	ROR AL, 1
register, CL	8 + 4/bit	—	2	ROR BX, CL
memory, 1	15 + EA	2	2-4	ROR PORT_STATUS, 1
memory, CL	20 + EA + 4/bit	2	2-4	ROR CMD_ WORD, CL

SAHF

SAHF (no operands) Store AH into flags				Flags	O D I T S Z A P C R R R R

Operands	Clocks	Transfers*	Bytes	Coding Example
(no operands)	4	—	1	SAHF

SAL/SHL

SAL/SHL destination,count Shift arithmetic left/Shift logical left				Flags	O D I T S Z A P C X X

Operands	Clocks	Transfers*	Bytes	Coding Examples
register,1	2	—	2	SAL AL,1
register, CL	8 + 4/bit	—	2	SHL DI, CL
memory,1	15 + EA	2	2-4	SHL [BX].OVERDRAW, 1
memory, CL	20 + EA + 4/bit	2	2-4	SAL STORE_ COUNT, CL

*For the 8086, add four clocks for each 16-bit word transfer with an odd address. For the 8088, add four clocks for each 16-bit word transfer.
Mnemonics © Intel, 1978

SAR	SAR destination,source Shift arithmetic right			Flags	O D I T S Z A P C X X X U X X
Operands	**Clocks**	**Transfers***	**Bytes**	**Coding Example**	
register, 1	2	—	2	SAR DX, 1	
register, CL	8 + 4 / bit	—	2	SAR DI, CL	
memory, 1	15 + EA	2	2-4	SAR N BLOCKS, 1	
memory, CL	20 + EA + 4 / bit	2	2-4	SAR N BLOCKS, CL	

SBB	SBB destination,source Subtract with borrow			Flags	O D I T S Z A P C X X X X X X
Operands	**Clocks**	**Transfers***	**Bytes**	**Coding Example**	
register, register	3	—	2	SBB BX, CX	
register, memory	9 + EA	1	2-4	SBB DI, [BX].PAYMENT	
memory, register	16 + EA	2	2-4	SBB BALANCE, AX	
accumulator, immediate	4	—	2-3	SBB AX, 2	
register, immediate	4	—	3-4	SBB CL, 1	
memory, immediate	17 + EA	2	3-6	SBB COUNT [SI], 10	

SCAS	SCAS dest-string Scan string			Flags	O D I T S Z A P C X X X X X X
Operands	**Clocks**	**Transfers***	**Bytes**	**Coding Example**	
dest-string	15	1	1	SCAS INPUT LINE	
(repeat) dest-string	9 + 15/rep	1/rep	1	REPNE SCAS BUFFER	

SEGMENT†	SEGMENT override prefix Override to specified segment			Flags	O D I T S Z A P C
Operands	**Clocks**	**Transfers***	**Bytes**	**Coding Example**	
(no operands)	2	—	1	MOV SS:PARAMETER, AX	

SHR	SHR destination,count Shift logical right			Flags	O D I T S Z A P C X X
Operands	**Clocks**	**Transfers***	**Bytes**	**Coding Example**	
register, 1	2	—	2	SHR SI, 1	
register, CL	8 + 4 / bit	—	2	SHR SI, CL	
memory, 1	15 + EA	2	2-4	SHR ID BYTE [SI] [BX], 1	
memory, CL	20 + EA + 4 / bit	2	2-4	SHR INPUT WORD, CL	

SINGLE STEP†	SINGLE STEP (Trap flag interrupt) Interrupt if TF = 1			Flags	O D I T S Z A P C 0 0
Operands	**Clocks**	**Transfers***	**Bytes**	**Coding Example**	
(no operands)	50	5	N/A	N/A	

*For the 8086, add four clocks for each 16-bit word transfer with an odd address. For the 8088, add four clocks for each 16-bit word transfer.

†ASM-86 incorporates the segment override prefix into the operand specification and not as a separate instruction. SEGMENT is included only for timing information.

†SINGLE STEP is not an instruction, it is included only for timing information.

Mnemonics © Intel, 1978

STC	STC (no operands) Set carry flag			Flags	O D I T S Z A P C 1
Operands	**Clocks**	**Transfers***	**Bytes**	**Coding Example**	
(no operands)	2	—	1	STC	

STD	STD (no operands) Set direction flag			Flags	O D I T S Z A P C 1
Operands	**Clocks**	**Transfers***	**Bytes**	**Coding Example**	
(no operands)	2	—	1	STD	

STI	STI (no operands) Set interrupt enable flag			Flags	O D I T S Z A P C 1
Operands	**Clocks**	**Transfers***	**Bytes**	**Coding Example**	
(no operands)	2	—	1	STI	

STOS	STOS dest-string Store byte or word string			Flags	O D I T S Z A P C
Operands	**Clocks**	**Transfers***	**Bytes**	**Coding Example**	
dest-string	11	1	1	STOS PRINT LINE	
(repeat) dest-string	9 + 10/rep	1/rep	1	REP STOS DISPLAY	

SUB	SUB destination,source Subtraction			Flags	O D I T S Z A P C X X X X X X
Operands	**Clocks**	**Transfers***	**Bytes**	**Coding Example**	
register, register	3	—	2	SUB CX, BX	
register, memory	9 + EA	1	2-4	SUB DX, MATH__TOTAL [SI]	
memory, register	16 + EA	2	2-4	SUB [BP + 2], CL	
accumulator, immediate	4	—	2-3	SUB AL, 10	
register, immediate	4	—	3-4	SUB SI, 5280	
memory, immediate	17 + EA	2	3-6	SUB [BP].BALANCE, 1000	

TEST	TEST destination,source Test or non-destructive logical and			Flags	O D I T S Z A P C 0 X X U X 0
Operands	**Clocks**	**Transfers***	**Bytes**	**Coding Example**	
register, register	3	—	2	TEST SI, DI	
register, memory	9 + EA	1	2-4	TEST SI, END__COUNT	
accumulator, immediate	4	—	2-3	TEST AL, 00100000B	
register, immediate	5	—	3-4	TEST BX, 0CC4H	
memory, immediate	11 + EA	—	3-6	TEST RETURN__CODE, 01H	

*For the 8086, add four clocks for each 16-bit word transfer with an odd address. For the 8088, add four clocks for each 16-bit word transfer.
Mnemonics © Intel, 1978

WAIT	WAIT (no operands) Wait while $\overline{\text{TEST}}$ pin not asserted		Flags	O D I T S Z A P C
Operands	**Clocks**	**Transfers***	**Bytes**	**Coding Example**
(no operands)	3 + 5n	—	1	WAIT

XCHG	XCHG destination,source Exchange		Flags	O D I T S Z A P C
Operands	**Clocks**	**Transfers***	**Bytes**	**Coding Example**
accumulator, reg16	3	—	1	XCHG AX, BX
memory, register	17 + EA	2	2-4	XCHG SEMAPHORE, AX
register, register	4	—	2	XCHG AL, BL

XLAT	XLAT source-table Translate		Flags	O D I T S Z A P C
Operands	**Clocks**	**Transfers***	**Bytes**	**Coding Example**
source-table	11	1	1	XLAT ASCII__TAB

XOR	XOR destination,source Logical exclusive or		Flags	O D I T S Z A P C 0 X X U X 0
Operands	**Clocks**	**Transfers***	**Bytes**	**Coding Example**
register, register	3	—	2	XOR CX, BX
register, memory	9 + EA	1	2-4	XOR CL, MASK__BYTE
memory, register	16 + EA	2	2-4	XOR ALPHA [SI], DX
accumulator, immediate	4	—	2-3	XOR AL, 01000010B
register, immediate	4	—	3-4	XOR SI, 00C2H
memory, immediate	17 + EA	2	3-6	XOR RETURN__CODE, 0D2H

*For the 8086, add four clocks for each 16-bit word transfer with an odd address. For the 8088, add four clocks for each 16-bit word transfer.
Mnemonics © Intel, 1978

INDEX

Selections from The SYBEX Library

SPREADSHEETS AND INTEGRATED SOFTWARE

The ABC's of 1-2-3 (Second Edition)
Chris Gilbert/Laurie Williams
245pp. Ref. 355-4
Online Today recommends it as "an easy and comfortable way to get started with the program." An essential tutorial for novices, it will remain on your desk as a valuable source of ongoing reference and support. For Release 2.

Mastering 1-2-3 (Second Edition)
Carolyn Jorgensen
500pp. Ref. 528-X
Get the most from 1-2-3 Release 2 with this step-by-step guide emphasizing advanced features and practical uses. Topics include data sharing, macros, spreadsheet security, expanded memory, and graphics enhancements.

Lotus 1-2-3 Desktop Companion (SYBEX Ready Reference Series)
Greg Harvey
976pp. Ref. 501-8
A full-time consultant, right on your desk. Hundreds of self-contained entries cover every 1-2-3 feature, organized by topic, indexed and cross-referenced, and supplemented by tips, macros and working examples. For Release 2.

Power User's Guide to Lotus 1-2-3
Peter Antoniak/E. Michael Lunsford
368pp. Ref. 421-6
This guide for experienced users focuses on advanced functions, and techniques for designing menu-driven applications using macros and the Release 2 command language. Interfacing techniques and add-on products are also considered.

Lotus 1-2-3 Instant Reference SYBEX Prompter Series
Greg Harvey/Kay Yarborough Nelson
296pp. Ref. 475-5; 4 3/4x8
Organized information at a glance. When you don't have time to hunt through hundreds of pages of manuals, turn here for a quick reminder: the right key sequence, a brief explanation of a command, or the correct syntax for a specialized function.

Mastering Lotus HAL
Mary V. Campbell
342pp. Ref. 422-4
A complete guide to using HAL "natural language" requests to communicate with 1-2-3—for new and experienced users. Covers all the basics, plus advanced HAL features such as worksheet linking and auditing, macro recording, and more.

Simpson's 1-2-3 Macro Library
Alan Simpson
298pp. Ref. 314-7
Increase productivity instantly with macros for custom menus, graphics, consolidating worksheets, interfacing with mainframes and more. With a tutorial on macro creation and details on Release 2 commands.

Mastering Symphony (Fourth Edition)
Douglas Cobb
875pp. Ref. 494-1
Thoroughly revised to cover all aspects of the major upgrade of Symphony Version 2, this Fourth Edition of Doug Cobb's classic is still "the Symphony bible" to this complex but even more powerful package. All the new features are discussed and placed in context with prior versions so that both new and previous users will benefit from Cobb's insights.

Focus on Symphony Macros
Alan Simpson
239pp. Ref. 351-1
An in-depth tutorial guide to creating, using, and debugging Symphony macros, including developing custom menus and automated systems, with an extensive library of useful ready-made macros for every Symphony module.

Focus on Symphony Databases
Alan Simpson/Donna M. Mosich
398pp. Ref. 336-8
Master every feature of this complex system by building real-life applications from the ground up—for mailing lists, inventory and accounts receivable. Everything from creating a first database to reporting, macros, and custom menus.

Better Symphony Spreadsheets
Carl Townsend
287pp. Ref. 339-2
Complete, in-depth treatment of the Symphony spreadsheet, stressing maximum power and efficiency. Topics include installation, worksheet design, data entry, formatting and printing, graphics, windows, and macros.

Mastering Quattro
Alan Simpson
400pp. Ref. 514-X
This tutorial covers not only all of Quattro's classic spreadsheet features, but also its added capabilities including extended graphing, modifiable menus, and the macro debugging environment. Simpson brings out how to use all of Quattro's new-generation-spreadsheet capabilities.

Mastering Framework II
Douglas Hergert/Jonathan Kamin
509pp. Ref. 390-2
This business-minded tutorial includes a complete introduction to idea processing, "frames," and software integration, along with its comprehensive treatment of word processing, spreadsheet, and database management with Framework.

Advanced Techniques in Framework: Programming in FRED
Alan Simpson
320pp. Ref. 246-9
This introduction to the FRED programming language is for experienced Framework users who need to expand their word processing, spreadsheet, graphics, and database management skills.

Mastering Excel on the IBM PC
Carl Townsend
550pp. Ref. 403-8
A complete Excel handbook with step-by-step tutorials, sample applications and an extensive reference section. Topics include worksheet fundamentals, formulas and windows, graphics, database techniques, special features, macros and more.

Mastering Enable
Keith D. Bishop
350pp. Ref. 440-2

A comprehensive, practical, hands-on guide to Enable 2.0—integrated word processing, spreadsheet, database management, graphics, and communications—from basic concepts to custom menus, macros and the Enable Procedural Language.

Mastering Q & A
Greg Harvey
399pp. Ref. 356-2

This hands-on tutorial explores the Q & A Write, File, and Report modules, and the Intelligent Assistant. English-language command processor, macro creation, interfacing with other software, and more, using practical business examples.

Mastering SuperCalc 4
Greg Harvey
311pp. Ref. 419-4

A guided tour of this spreadsheet, database and graphics package shows how and why it adds up to a powerful business planning tool. Step-by-step lessons and real-life examples cover every aspect of the program.

Understanding Javelin PLUS
John R. Levine
Margaret Levine Young
Jordan M. Young
558pp. Ref. 358-9

This detailed guide to Javelin's latest release includes a concise introduction to business modeling, from profit-and-loss analysis to manufacturing studies. Readers build sample models and produce multiple reports and graphs, to master Javelin's unique features.

DATABASE MANAGEMENT

Mastering Paradox (Third Edition)
Alan Simpson
600pp. Ref. 490-9

Paradox is given authoritative, comprehensive explanation in Simpson's up-to-date new edition which goes from database basics to command-file programming with PAL. Topics include multiuser networking, the Personal Programmer Application Generator, the Data-Entry Toolkit, and more.

Mastering Reflex
Robert Ericson/Ann Moskol
336pp. Ref. 348-1

A complete introduction to Reflex: The Analyst, with hands-on tutorials and sample applications for management, finance, and technical uses. Special emphasis on its unique capabilities for crosstabbing, graphics, reporting, and more.

dBASE III PLUS Programmer's Reference Guide (SYBEX Ready Reference Series)
Alan Simpson
1056pp. Ref. 508-5

Programmers will save untold hours and effort using this comprehensive, well-organized dBASE encyclopedia. Complete technical details on commands and functions, plus scores of often-needed algorithms.

The ABC's of dBASE III PLUS
Robert Cowart
264pp. Ref. 379-1

The most efficient way to get beginners up and running with dBASE. Every 'how' and 'why' of database management is demonstrated through tutorials and practical dBASE III PLUS applications.

Mastering dBASE III PLUS: A Structured Approach
Carl Townsend
342pp. Ref. 372-4
In-depth treatment of structured programming for custom dBASE solutions. An ideal study and reference guide for applications developers, new and experienced users with an interest in efficient programming.

Also:
Mastering dBASE III: A Structured Approach
Carl Townsend
338pp. Ref. 301-5

Understanding dBASE III PLUS
Alan Simpson
415pp. Ref. 349-X
A solid sourcebook of training and ongoing support. Everything from creating a first database to command file programming is presented in working examples, with tips and techniques you won't find anywhere else.

Also:
Understanding dBASE III
Alan Simpson
300pp. Ref. 267-1

Understanding dBASE II
Alan Simpson
260pp. Ref. 147-0

Advanced Techniques in dBASE III PLUS
Alan Simpson
454pp. Ref. 369-4
A full course in database design and structured programming, with routines for inventory control, accounts receivable, system management, and integrated databases.

Also:
Advanced Techniques in dBASE III
Alan Simpson
505pp. Ref.282-5

Advanced Techniques in dBASE II
Alan Simpson
395pp. Ref. 228-0

Simpson's dBASE Tips and Tricks (For dBASE III PLUS)
Alan Simpson
420pp. Ref. 383-X
A unique library of techniques and programs shows how creative use of built-in features can solve all your needs – without expensive add-on products or external languages. Spreadsheet functions, graphics, and much more.

Expert dBASE III PLUS
Judd Robbins/Ken Braly
423pp. Ref. 404-6
Experienced dBASE programmers learn scores of advanced techniques for maximizing performance and efficiency in program design, development and testing, database design, indexing, input and output, using compilers, and much more.

dBASE Instant Reference SYBEX Prompter Series
Alan Simpson
471pp. Ref. 484-4; 4 3/4x8
Comprehensive information at a glance: a brief explanation of syntax and usage for every dBASE command, with step-by-step instructions and exact keystroke sequences. Commands are grouped by function in twenty precise categories.

Understanding R:BASE System V
Alan Simpson
499pp. Ref. 394-5
This complete tutorial guide covers every R:BASE function, while exploring and illustrating the principles of efficient database design. Examples include inventory management, mailing list handling, and much more.

Also:
Understanding R:BASE 5000
Alan Simpson
413pp. Ref. 302-3

GENERAL UTILITIES

The ABC's of the IBM PC
Joan Lasselle/Carol Ramsay
143pp. Ref. 102-0
Hands-on experience – without technical detail – for first-time users. Step-by-step tutorials show how to use essential commands, handle disks, use applications programs, and harness the PC's special capabilities.

Mastering ThinkTank on the IBM PC
Jonathan Kamin
350pp. Ref. 327-9
A business-minded tutorial on "idea processing" with ThinkTank – from first outlines to advanced features. Examples include logging sales calls, maintaining a resume, and creating a marketing plan. With complete reference sections.

COMPUTER-AIDED DESIGN AND DRAFTING

The ABC's of AutoCAD
Alan R. Miller
350pp. Ref. 498-4
This brief but effective introduction to AutoCAD quickly gets users drafting and designing with this complex CADD package. The essential operations and capabilities of AutoCAD are neatly detailed, using a proven, step-by-step method that is tailored to the results-oriented beginner.

Mastering AutoCAD (Second Edition)
George Omura
650pp. Ref. 502-6
Now in its second edition, this tutorial guide to computer-aided design and drafting with AutoCAD is perfect for newcomers to CADD, as well as AutoCAD users seeking greater proficiency. An architectural project serves as an example throughout.

Advanced Techniques in AutoCAD
Robert M. Thomas
410pp. Ref. 437-2
Develop custom applications using screen menus, command macros, and AutoLISP programming – no prior programming experience required. Topics include customizing the AutoCAD environment, advanced data extraction techniques, and much more.

FOR SCIENTISTS AND ENGINEERS

1-2-3 for Scientists and Engineers
William J. Orvis
341pp. Ref. 407-0
Fast, elegant solutions to common problems in science and engineering, using Lotus 1-2-3. Tables and plotting, curve fitting, statistics, derivatives, integrals and differentials, solving systems of equations, and more.

BASIC Programs for Scientists and Engineers
Alan R. Miller
318pp. Ref. 073-3
The algorithms presented in this book are programmed in standard BASIC code which should be usable with almost any implementation of BASIC. Includes statistical calculations, matrix algebra, curve fitting, integration, and more.

Turbo BASIC Programs for Scientists and Engineers
Alan R. Miller
276pp. Ref. 429-1
This practical text develops commonly-needed algorithms for scientific and engineering applications, and programs them in Turbo BASIC. Simultaneous solution, curve fitting, nonlinear equations, numerical integration and more.

Pascal Programs for Scientists and Engineers
Alan R. Miller
374pp. Ref. 058-X
Programming techniques are included for curve fitting, vector and matrix calculations, numerical integration, random number generation, statistical analysis, and more.

Turbo Pascal Programs for Scientists and Engineers
Alan R. Miller
332pp. Ref. 424-0
The author develops commonly-needed algorithms for science and engineering, then programs them in Turbo Pascal. Includes algorithms for statistics, simultaneous solutions, curve fitting, integration, and nonlinear equations.

FORTRAN Programs for Scientists and Engineers
Alan R. Miller
280pp. Ref. 082-2
In this collection of widely used scientific algorithms – for statistics, vector and matrix operations, curve fitting, and more – the author stresses effective use of little-known and powerful features of FORTRAN.

WORD PROCESSING

The ABC's of WordPerfect (Second Edition)
Alan R. Neibauer
300pp. Ref. 504-2
This introduction explains the basics of desktop publishing with WordPerfect 5: editing, layout, formatting, printing, sorting, merging, and more. Readers are shown how to use WordPerfect 5's new features to produce great-looking reports.

The ABC's of WordPerfect
Alan R. Neibauer
239pp. Ref. 425-9
This basic introduction to WordPefect consists of short, step-by-step lessons— for new users who want to get going fast. Topics range from simple editing and formatting, to merging, sorting, macros, and more. Includes version 4.2

Mastering WordPerfect 5
Susan Baake Kelly
475pp. Ref. 500-X
The revised and expanded version of this definitive guide is now on WordPerfect 5 and covers wordprocessing and basic desktop publishing. As more than 100,000 readers of the original edition can attest, no tutorial approaches it for clarity and depth of treatment. Sorting, line drawing, and laser printing included.

Mastering WordPerfect
Susan Baake Kelly
435pp. Ref. 332-5
Step-by-step training from startup to mastery, featuring practical uses (form letters, newsletters and more), plus advanced topics such as document security and macro creation, sorting and columnar math. Includes Version 4.2.

Advanced Techniques in WordPerfect 5
Kay Yarborough Nelson
500pp. Ref. 511-5
Now updated for Version 5, this invaluable guide to the advanced features of WordPerfect provides step-by-step instructions and practical examples covering those specialized techniques which have most perplexed users – indexing, outlining, foreign-language typing, mathematical functions, and more.

Advanced Techniques in WordPerfect
Kay Yarborough Nelson
400pp. Ref. 431-3

Exact details are presented on how to accomplish complex tasks including special sorts, layered indexing, and statistical typing. Includes details on laser printing operations.

WordPerfect Desktop Companion
SYBEX Ready Reference Series
Greg Harvey/Kay Yarbourough Nelson
663pp. Ref. 507-7

This compact encyclopedia offers detailed, cross-referenced entries on every software feature, organized for fast, convenient on-the-job help. Includes self-contained enrichment material with tips, techniques and macros. Special information is included about laser printing using WordPerfect that is not available elsewhere. For Version 4.2.

WordPerfect 5 Desktop Companion
SYBEX Ready Reference Series
Greg Harvey/Kay Yarborough Nelson
700pp. Ref. 522-0

Desktop publishing features have been added to this compact encyclopedia. This title offers more detailed, cross-referenced entries on every software features including page formatting and layout, laser printing and word processing macros. New users of WordPerfect, and those new to Version 5 and desktop publishing will find this easy to use for on-the-job help. For Version 5.

WordPerfect Tips and Tricks (Second Edition)
Alan R. Neibauer
488pp. Ref. 489-5

This new edition is a real timesaver. For on-the-job guidance and creative new uses for WordPerfect, this title covers all new features of Version 4.2 – including tables of authorities, concordance files, new print enhancements and more.

WordPerfect Instant Reference
SYBEX Prompter Series
Greg Harvey/Kay Yarborough Nelson
254pp. Ref. 476-3

When you don't have time to go digging through the manuals, this fingertip guide offers clear, concise answers: command summaries, correct usage, and exact keystroke sequences for on-the-job tasks. Convenient organization reflects the structure of WordPerfect.

Mastering SAMNA
Ann McFarland Draper
503pp. Ref. 376-7

Word-processing professionals learn not just how, but also when and why to use SAMNA's many powerful features. Master the basics, gain power-user skills, return again and again for reference and expert tips.

The ABC's of MicroSoft WORD
Alan R. Neibauer
250pp. Ref. 497-6

Users who want to wordprocess straightforward documents and print elegant reports without wading through reams of documentation will find all they need to know about MicroSoft WORD in this basic guide. Simple editing, formatting, merging, sorting, macros and style sheets are detailed.

Mastering Microsoft WORD (Second Edition)
Matthew Holtz
479pp. Ref. 410-0

This comprehensive, step-by-step guide includes Version 3.1. Hands-on tutorials treat everything from word processing basics to the fundamentals of desktop publishing, stressing business applications throughout.

Advanced Techinques in Microsoft WORD
Alan R. Neibauer
537pp. Ref. 416-X
The book starts with a brief overview, but the main focus is on practical applications using advanced features. Topics include customization, forms, style sheets, columns, tables, financial documents, graphics and data management.

Mastering DisplayWrite 3
Michael E. McCarthy
447pp. Ref. 340-6
Total training, reference and support for users at all levels – in plain, non-technical language. Novices will be up and running in an hour's time; everyone will gain complete word-processing and document-management skills.

Mastering MultiMate Advantage II
Charles Ackerman
407pp. Ref. 482-8
This comprehensive tutorial covers all the capabilities of MultiMate, and highlights the differences between MultiMate Advantage II and previous versions – in pathway support, sorting, math, DOS access, using dBASE III, and more. With many practical examples, and a chapter on the On-File database.

Mastering MultiMate Advantage
Charles Ackerman
349pp. Ref. 380-5
Master much more than simple word processing by making the most of your software. Sample applications include creating expense reports, maintaining customer lists, merge-printing complex documents and more.

The Complete Guide to MultiMate
Carol Holcomb Dreger
208pp. Ref. 229-9
This step-by-step tutorial is also an excellent reference guide to MultiMate features and uses. Topics include search/replace, library and merge functions, repagination, document defaults and more.

Advanced Techniques in MultiMate
Chris Gilbert
275pp. Ref. 412-7
A textbook on efficient use of MultiMate for business applications, in a series of self-contained lessons on such topics as multiple columns, high-speed merging, mailing-list printing and Key Procedures.

The ABC's of WordStar Release 5
Alan Simpson
300pp. Ref. 516-6
This quick guide to getting started on WordStar Release 5's full capabilities covers editing, formatting, printing good-looking documents and more detailed word processing tasks. Ideal for the new user who wants an uncomplicated introduction.

Mastering WordStar Release 5
Greg Harvey
425pp. Ref. 491-7
Harvey's complete tutorial and reference guide covers all the features of WordStar Release 5 from elementary to advanced, and highlights functions new to this release. Better document processing, editing, and printing are emphasized throughout with examples.

Introduction to WordStar (Second Edition)
Arthur Naiman
208pp. Ref. 134-9
This all time bestseller is an engaging first-time introduction to word processing as well as a complete guide to using WordStar – from basic editing to blocks, global searches, formatting, dot commands, SpellStar and MailMerge.

Practical Techniques in WordStar Release 5
Julie Anne Arca
350pp. Ref. 495-X
Arca's classic is fully revised to cover WordStar 5's latest features. Designed to lead readers through step-by-step examples and exercises, this user-friendly title has sold over 100,000 copies in the original edition.

Mastering Wordstar on the IBM PC (Second Edition)
Arthur Naiman
200pp. Ref. 392-9
A specially revised and expanded introduction to Wordstar with SpellStar and MailMerge. Reviewers call it "clearly written, conveniently organized, generously illustrated and definitely designed from the user's point of view."

Practical WordStar Uses
Julie Anne Arca
303pp. Ref. 107-1
A hands-on guide to WordStar and MailMerge applications, with solutions to comon problems and "recipes" for day-to-day tasks. Formatting, merge-printing and much more; plus a quick-reference command chart and notes on CP/M and PC-DOS.

Practical Techniques in WordStar Release 4
Julie Anne Arca
334pp. Ref. 465-8
A task oriented approach to WordStar Release 4 and the DOS operating system. Special applications are covered in detail with summaries of important commands and step-by-step instructions.

WordStar Tips and Traps
Dick Andersen/Cynthia Cooper/Janet McBeen
239pp. Ref. 261-2
A real time-saver. Hundreds of self-contained entries, arranged by topic, cover everything from customization to dealing with the DISK FULL error to keystroke programming. Includes MailMerge and CorrectStar.

Mastering WordStar Release 4
Greg Harvey
413pp. Ref. 399-6
Practical training and reference for the latest WordStar release – from startup to advanced featues. Experienced users will find new features highlighted and illustrated with hands-on examples. Covers math, macros, laser printers and more.

Introduction to WordStar 2000
David Kolodney/Thomas Blackadar
292pp. Ref. 270-1
This engaging, fast-paced series of tutorials covers everything from moving the cursor to print enhancements, format files, key glossaries, windows and MailMerge. With practical examples, and notes for former WordStar users.

Advanced Techniques in WordStar 2000
John Donovan
350pp. Ref. 418-6
This task-oriented guide to Release 2 builds advanced skills by developing practical applications. Tutorials cover everything from simple printing to macro creation and complex merging. With MailList, StarIndex and TelMerge.

DESKTOP PUBLISHING

Mastering Ventura
Matthew Holtz
546pp. Ref. 427-5
A complete, step-by-step guide to IBM PC desktop publishing with Xerox Ventura Publisher. Practical examples show how to use style sheets, format pages, cut and paste, enhance layouts, import material from other programs, and more.

Mastering PageMaker on the IBM PC
Antonia Stacy Jolles
287pp. Ref. 393-7
A guide to every aspect of desktop publishing with PageMaker: the vocabulary and basics of page design, layout, graphics and typography, plus instructions for creating finished typeset publications of all kinds.

SYBEX Computer Books
are different.

Here is why . . .

At SYBEX, each book is designed with you in mind. Every manuscript is carefully selected and supervised by our editors, who are themselves computer experts. We publish the best authors, whose technical expertise is matched by an ability to write clearly and to communicate effectively. Programs are thoroughly tested for accuracy by our technical staff. Our computerized production department goes to great lengths to make sure that each book is well-designed.

In the pursuit of timeliness, SYBEX has achieved many publishing firsts. SYBEX was among the first to integrate personal computers used by authors and staff into the publishing process. SYBEX was the first to publish books on the CP/M operating system, microprocessor interfacing techniques, word processing, and many more topics.

Expertise in computers and dedication to the highest quality product have made SYBEX a world leader in computer book publishing. Translated into fourteen languages, SYBEX books have helped millions of people around the world to get the most from their computers. We hope we have helped you, too.

For a complete catalog of our publications:

SYBEX, Inc. 2021 Challenger Drive, #100, Alameda, CA 94501
Tel: (415) 523-8233/(800) 227-2346   Telex: 336311